Electronic Hobbyists Handbook

ALSO OF INTEREST

BP234	Transistor Selector Guide
BP235	Power Selector Guide
BP236	Digital IC Selector Guide — Part 1
BP237	Digital IC Selector Guide — Part 2
BP238	Linear IC Selector Guide
BP140	Digital IC Equivalents and Pin Connections
BP141	Linear IC Equivalents and Pin Connections
BP85	International Transistor Equivalents Guide
BP108	International Diode Equivalents Guide
BP101	How to Identify Unmarked ICs
BP7	Radio and Electronic Colour Codes and Data Chart
BP27	Chart of Radio, Electronic, Semiconductor and Logic Symbols
BP117	Practical Electronic Building Blocks — Book 1
BP118	Practical Electronic Building Blocks — Book 2
BP127	How to Design Electronic Projects
BP130	Micro Interfacing Circuits — Book 1
BP131	Micro Interfacing Circuits — Book 2
BP44	IC 555 Projects
BP88	How to Use Op-Amps
BP106	Modern Op-Amp Projects

For details on how to obtain a FREE CATALOGUE of our entire range of Radio, Electronics and Computer books, see page 88.

Electronic Hobbyists Handbook

by
R.A. Penfold

BERNARD BABANI (publishing) LTD
THE GRAMPIANS
SHEPHERDS BUSH ROAD
LONDON W6 7NF
ENGLAND

PLEASE NOTE

Although every care has been taken with the production of this book to ensure that any information, projects, designs, modifications and/or programs etc. contained herewith, operate in a correct and safe manner and also that any components specified are normally available in Great Britain, the Publishers do not accept responsibility in any way for the failure, including fault in design, of any information, project, design, modification or program to work correctly or to cause damage to any other equipment that it may be connected to or used in conjunction with, or in respect of any other damage or injury that may be so caused, nor do the Publishers accept responsibility in any way for the failure to obtain specified components.

Notice is also given that if equipment that is still under warranty is modified in any way or used or connected with home-built equipment then that warranty may be void.

First Published — November 1987
Reprinted — March 1989

British Library Cataloguing in Publication Data
Penfold, R.A.
    Electronic hobbyists handbook.
    1. Electronics
    I. Title
    537.5   TK7815

ISBN 0 85934 178 X

Printed and Bound by The Guernsey Press Co. Ltd, Channel Islands

PREFACE

The hobby of electronics can be a bewildering one at times, and there seems to be an ever increasing range of components and types of circuit for them to operate in. Associated with these components and circuits is a mass of data; some of a mundane nature such as details of the resistor colour codes, and some of a more specialised nature (data for a dedicated integrated circuit for an unusual application for example). Most electronics hobbyists soon start to accumulate data from sources such as books, magazines, and electronic component catalogues. This then leaves the problem of locating the particular piece of data that is required, if it is actually present in the collection.

The aim of this book is to provide a useful collection of data for the amateur electronics enthusiast, so that much of the data he or she will require is available in a single source where it can be quickly and easily located. I will not claim that all the data the average electronics hobbyist will ever need can be found between the covers of this book, but there is a great deal of data on likely topics of interest, including colour codes, integrated circuit pinouts, transistor leadout diagrams and data, basic circuit building blocks, etc. The aim of this book is not to provide a course in electronics, and some knowledge of electronics is needed in order to make use of much of the data. However, in most cases the reader is not simply provided with raw details, and where appropriate background information and explanatory notes are provided.

R. A. Penfold

CONTENTS

	Page
COLOUR CODES	1
Resistors	1
Five Band Codes	1
Capacitors	3
Tantalum Bead	4
Ceramics	5
Inductors	5
LOGIC ICs	6
TTL	6
CMOS	6
LS TTL	7
HC CMOS	7
FACT	7
The Field	8
Mixing	8
Pinouts	9
TTL ICs Function and Package	17
CMOS ICs Function and Package	20
POWER SUPPLIES	22
Rectification	22
Regulators	24
Series Regulators	26
Variable Regulators	27
Three Terminal	27
Current Regulators	28
Rectifier Pinout Details	29
CIRCUIT SYMBOLS	31
OPERATIONAL AMPLIFIERS	35
Modes	35
Offset Null	38
Other Parameters	38
Slew Rate	38
Large Signal Bandwidth	38
Common Mode Rejection	39
Latch-Up	39
Output Voltage Swing	39
Output Resistance	39
Table of Basic Data	40
Pinouts	42
TRANSISTORS	45
Parameters	45
Amplifying Modes	46
Darlington Pairs	48
Type Numbers	49
Pro Electron	49
Gain Groups	49
JEDEC Codes	49
JIS Codes	50
Manufacturers Digits	50
Table of Small and Medium Power Audio Transistor Characteristics	51
Table of Small and Medium Power Radio Frequency Transistor Characteristics	54

Page

Table of Power Device Characteristics 55
Field Effect Devices 56
Parameters 57
Unijunctions 58
Table of Small Signal FET Characteristics 59
Table of Power FET Characteristics 59
Table of Unijunction Characteristics 62
Power Transistor Pinout Details 62
Small FET Leadout Details 63
Power FET Connection Details 63
UJT Leadouts 64

OTHER SEMICONDUCTORS 65
Diodes 65
Varicap Diodes 65
SCRs 65
Table of Diode Characteristics 66
Table of Varicap Diode Characteristics 66
SCR Parameters 67
Table of Thyristor Characteristics 68
Triacs 68
Diacs 68
Thyristor Pinout Details 68
Table of Triac Characteristics 69
Triac Pinout Details 69

SURFACE MOUNTING DEVICES 70
Density 71
Home Construction 71

USEFUL CIRCUITS 73
555 73
CMOS 74
Audio Amplifiers 75
Filters 76

CENTRONICS INTERFACE 79

RS232C INTERFACE 80

AMATEUR BAND ALLOCATIONS 81
Short Wave 81
V.H.F. 81

CB FREQUENCY ALLOCATIONS 82
27 MHz Band 82
934 MHz Band 82

AMATEUR ABBREVIATIONS 83

Q CODES 84

SINPO 85

MORSE CODE 86

FREQUENCY-WAVELENGTH CONVERSION 87

COLOUR CODES

Deciphering colour codes is something that tends to cause a certain amount of difficulty to most electronics hobbyists from time to time. Although they can be awkward at times with colours being less than obvious and several methods of coding to help confuse matters, for small components this method is almost certainly better than simply having the values written on the bodies of the components. A component has to be seriously damaged before most types of colour are rendered unreadable, but with values written on in ordinary alpha-numeric characters it only takes minor damage to make the value undecipherable. Worse still, with values written on components in ordinary characters it is quite common for the writing to become slightly defaced, resulting in an apparent marked value which is far removed from the true one. Another advantage of colour codes is that once you have become used to them it is quite easy to pick out a component of the required value from a box of mixed values without having to look carefully at each component until you come across one with the right value.

Resistors

Colour codes are used for both resistors and capacitors, but whereas few types of capacitor have this method of value markings these days, with resistors there are few types that do not. There are several forms of resistor colour coding, but they are really all just variations on the basic scheme of things. Figure 1 provides details of four types of resistor colour coding.

The four band coding of Figure 1(a) is the standard type which is still used for the vast majority of small resistors. Band 1, which is the one nearest to one end of the component, provides the first digit, band 2 indicates the second digit, and band 3 is the multiplier. Finally, band 4 gives the component's tolerance. The table provided here shows what values each colour corresponds to for each band.

Colour	Band 1	Band 2	Band 3	Band 4
Silver	–	–	x0.01	10%
Gold	–	–	x0.1	5%
Black	0	0	x1	–
Brown	1	1	x10	1%
Red	2	2	x100	2%
Orange	3	3	x1000	–
Yellow	4	4	x10000	–
Green	5	5	x100000	–
Blue	6	6	x1000000	–
Violet	7	7	–	–
Grey	8	8	–	–
White	9	9	–	–
None	–	–	–	20%

If we take a couple of simple examples to illustrate how the system operates, a resistor with the colour coding 'brown – black – orange – gold', would be a 10k 5% type. The brown band indicates that the first digit is '1', while the black second band shows that the next digit is '0'. This gives '10', which is multiplied by 1000, as indicated by the next band which is orange. 10 x 1000 is obviously 10000 ohms, or 10k as this value would normally be expressed. A convenient way of handling the multiplier band is to take its band 1 or band 2 value, and then add this many zeros to the first two digits. In this example we have '10' for the first two digits, and with orange as the multiplier three zeros would therefore be added to it to give '10000', which again gives us 10k as the value. Of course, this simple dodge is not usable with silver or gold as the multipliers, as these are not used for bands 1 and 2. The gold band as the fourth and final one indicates that the tolerance is 5%, giving a total value of 10k plus or minus 5%.

'Red – red – gold – gold' would indicate that the first two digits are '2' and '2', and the gold third band indicates that these should be multiplied by 0.1. 22 x 0.1 is obviously 2.2, giving a value of 2.2 ohms. The gold final band again indicates a tolerance of plus and minus 5%.

Five Band Codes

The five band coding of Figure 1(b) is very little different to the four band variety, with the extra band merely enabling an extra digit to be used at the beginning of the value. This is a method of coding that is only used with close tolerance (1% or better) resistors where the greater precision of the extra digit can be justified. With this five band coding a value such as 49.3k can be indicated, which is impossible with the ordinary four band type. Note though, that in amateur electronics odd values of this type are not normally available as resistors (and certain other components) are only generally available in "preferred" values. Details of what have become known as the E6, E12 and E24 series of preferred values are provided below:—

E6	E12	E24
1	1	1
–	–	1.1
–	1.2	1.2
–	–	1.3
1.5	1.5	1.5
–	–	1.6
–	1.8	1.8
–	–	2
2.2	2.2	2.2
–	–	2.4
–	2.7	2.7
–	–	3
3.3	3.3	3.3

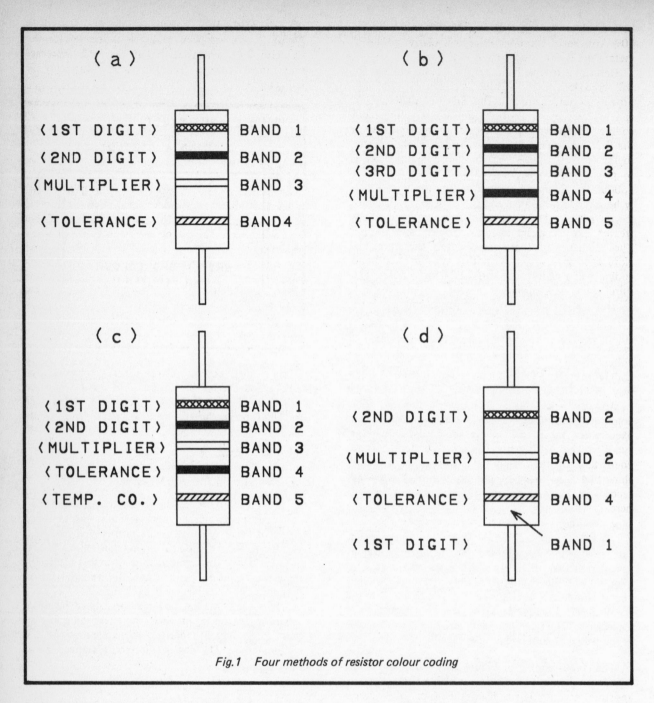

Fig.1   Four methods of resistor colour coding

E6	E12	E24
—	—	3.6
—	3.9	3.9
—	—	4.3
4.7	4.7	4.7
—	—	5.1
—	5.6	5.6
—	—	6.2
6.8	6.8	6.8
—	—	7.5
—	8.2	8.2
—	—	9.1
10	10	10

E6	E12	E24
—	—	11
—	12	12
—	—	13
—	15	15
—	—	16
etc.	etc.	etc.

With the E24 series of values each one is about 10% higher than the previous one, and this series is only applicable to components which offer a tolerance of plus and minus 5% or better. The E12 series is suitable for components with a tolerance of 10% or better, while the E6 series is generally only used for 20% tolerance components (particularly potentiometers and electrolytic capacitors).

Returning to five band resistor colour coding, we will consider 'green – blue – black – yellow – brown' as our example. The first two digits are '5' and '6', as they would be in the ordinary four band coding. The third band is treated in the same way as the first two, giving '0' as the third digit and a value so far of '560'. This must be multiplied by 10000, to give a total value of 5600000 (560 x 10000 = 5600000). A large value of this type would normally be given in megohms, and is 5.6 megohms or '5M6' if you prefer. The final band is 'brown', and this is treated like the final band of a four band coding. The tolerance of the component is therefore 1%. Note that as resistors with this type of five band coding will usually only carry E24 series values the third digit will probably always be 'black' ('0').

There is an alternative five band resistor colour code, as shown in Figure 1(c). This is rather unfortunate in that it is possible to be confronted with a resistor that has a valid coding for either form of five colour coding. You may know which method of coding the component carries, but if not the only way to determine its value would be to measure it.

Anyway, with this second system the first four coloured bands indicate the value and tolerance in exactly the same way as the standard four colour type. The fifth band shows the temperature coefficient of the component. This is not something that is normally of any importance, but for the record details of this fifth band coding are provided here.

Colour	Temp Co. (ppm/degree C)
Black	200
Brown	100
Red	50
Yellow	25
Orange	15
Blue	10
Violet	5
Grey	1

The colour coding of Figure 1(d) is well and truly obsolete, although there may well be some surplus resistors around which have this type of coding. There are certainly plenty of older items of equipment around which have resistors which carry this type of coding. It is basically the same as the ordinary four band type, but the first band has been omitted, and instead the colour of the component's body provides the code for the first digit in the value.

There is yet another form of colour coding, and this is another one which seems to be obsolete. However, once again, resistors having this type of coding do still turn up from time to time, and may be encountered in older items of equipment. As far as I am aware, it is a system that is only used for high power resistors (about 3 watts and upwards). Details

of this method of colour coding are shown in Figure 2. It works in much the same way as the standard four band type, but in this case there are only three colours and no tolerance value is indicated.

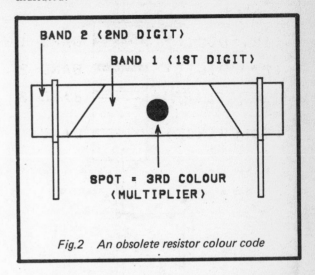

Fig.2   An obsolete resistor colour code

Many high power resistors (over 1 watt) do not have colour codes these days, but have the value written on using a letter to indicate the units in use and the position of the decimal point. The letters used are as follows:—

R	Ohms
k	Kilohms
M	Megohms

Thus, a 2.2 ohm resistor would be marked '2R2', or a 33k type would be marked '33k'. The wattage rating of small resistors is not normally included in any form of marking on the component, although the physical size of these components gives a fair guide to their power rating. It is normally included in the markings on higher power types though.

There are some low power resistors that have the value written on in this way, and there is usually an extra digit which indicates the tolerance of the component. The list of letters/tolerances is as follows:—

F	1%
G	2%
J	5%
K	10%
H	20%

Small resistors having this method of marking are something of a rarity these days though, and the vast majority of these components have four or five band colour coding.

Capacitors

Although at one time colour coding was quite common on capacitors there are currently relatively few types which use this type of value marking. In fact

3

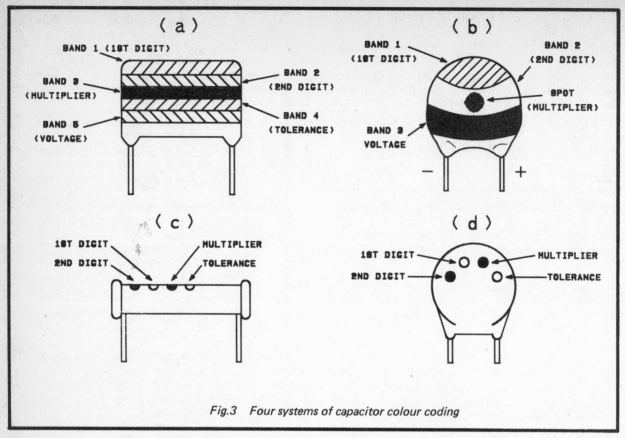

Fig.3   Four systems of capacitor colour coding

the only type of capacitor where it is at all common is the 'C280' style polyester type. Not all these still use this method though. Figure 3 provides details of four types of capacitor colour coding, including the C280 variety in Figure 3(a).

As far as the value is concerned, this operates in exactly the same manner as the ordinary four band resistor colour coding, with the first three colours respectively indicating the first digit, second digit, and multiplier. Of course, the value is not in ohms, it is in picofarads. The figure obtained from the colour code must therefore be divided by 1000 to give an answer in nanofarads, or by 1000000 to give a value in microfarads.

The fourth band indicates the tolerance, but not using the standard resistor colour codes. The fifth band shows the maximum working voltage of the component. Details of the fourth and fifth band colour codes are provided below:—

Colour	Band 4	Band 5
Black	20%	–
White	10%	–
Green	5%	–
Orange	2.5%	–
Red	2%	250V
Brown	1%	–
Yellow	–	400V

Most of the C280 capacitors you obtain will be 250 volt types, but there are some 400 volt types around. Values of 220nF or less are generally 20% tolerance with higher values having a tolerance of 10%. The last two bands will therefore be black and red or white and red in the majority of cases.

Tantalum Bead

Tantalum capacitors, or tantalum "beads" as they are often called (presumably due to their bead-like shape) at one time almost invariably used colour coding, but many do not these days. This is perhaps a shame since they are generally quite small components. The most common form of colour coding for tantalum capacitors is shown in Figure 3(b). The way in which the first three digits indicate the value of the component is very similar to the standard four band resistor colour code system, but it is not identical. The fourth band indicates the maximum operating voltage. Details of the colours used and their meaning in each band is shown in this table:—

Colour	Band 1	Band 2	Band 3	Band 4
Black	–	0	x1	10V
Brown	1	1	x10	–
Red	2	2	x100	–
Orange	3	3	–	–
Yellow	4	4	–	6V3
Green	5	5	–	16V
Blue	6	6	–	20V
Violet	7	7	–	–
Grey	8	8	x0.01	25V
White	9	9	x0.1	3V
Pink	–	–	–	35V

An important point to note here is that the value is in microfarads, and not picofarads (as with the C280 system). To convert the value to nanofarads multiply by 1000, or multiply it by 1000000 in the unlikely event that you want the value in picofarads. Note that with this system of coding the polarity of the component is not indicated by the usual '+' and '−' signs. Instead, with the coloured spot facing towards you the positive lead is the one on the right and the negative lead is the one on the left.

Ceramics

Some ceramic capacitors (mainly fairly low value types) use a system of colour coding. The tubular style use the system detailed in Figure 3(c) while the more common disc ceramic type use what is essentially the same system, and is detailed in Figure 3(d). In both cases the value in picofarads is indicated in standard four band resistor colour code fashion. A few components which have this method of coding use five dots with the first one indicating the temperature coefficient. If the first spot is ignored the remaining four then indicate the value in the standard fashion.

Inductors

It is increasingly common for radio frequency chokes to have their values marked using a colour code. This system of coding is actually the same as the standard four band resistor colour code though, and it should not cause any real difficulties. The value is given in nanohenries, and must be divided by 1000 to give an answer in microhenries.

Although it is not that many years ago that logic integrated circuits in electronic designs for the home constructor were non-existent, they have steadily appeared in an increasing number of projects. We are now at the stage where there seems to be relatively few designs that do not use at least one of these devices, and they quite often appear in circuits that are primarily linear in nature. Not only do these devices appear frequently in electronic designs, but there is an ever wider selection of available types. This is partially due to totally new devices appearing, but probably most new devices are 'improved' versions of existing devices. In fact there are now several families of 'improved' devices, of which the standard CMOS (4000 series) and low-power Schottky (74LS00 series) are the best known. These two logic families have rendered the original 7400 series virtually obsolete, and the standard TTL devices are rarely used in new designs. The original rivals to the 7400 TTL family (such as the DTL and RTL chips) have long since been obsolete.

Choosing logic integrated has become a rather confusing subject with so many different versions to choose from, and many hobbyists simply stick to the familiar types rather than risking 'improved' devices which might simply prove to be costly mistakes. It can also be difficult to find out just what alternatives can be substituted for a given device without impairing the performance of a circuit, or even causing it to fail altogether. We will take a quick look here at the various logic families that are available, and how they differ in terms of performance. A table of characteristics is provided and this summarises the information and puts it in an easily accessible form. However, the information provided here is necessarily a generalization, and it can do no more than give a rough guide to the speed etc. of the various logic families. Individual devices within each family tend to have slightly different propagation delays, maximum operating frequencies, etc., and for detailed information the appropriate data book or data sheet must be consulted.

TTL

The standard TTL devices obviously provide a reasonable standard of performance or they would never have been used on such a vast scale. On the other hand, they must have deficiencies or they would not have been ousted by subsequent logic families. Probably their most serious problem is a fairly high level of current consumption, with a few gates being sufficient to consume around 50 to 100 milliamps. With some of the more complex devices the current consumption is around 100 milliamps per device. They are also rather fussy about the supply voltage, with a requirement of 5 volts plus or minus 5%. Perhaps of greater significance, they are very intolerant of noise spikes on the supply rails, and circuits using these devices generally have a large number of supply decoupling capacitors scattered around the circuit board. Standard TTL devices are quite fast and can handle frequencies of up to around 30 to 40 MHz.

CMOS

CMOS (complementary metal oxide silicon) devices overcome many of the drawbacks of standard TTL devices, but in the process add some more of their own. Their main claim to fame is their extremely low static current consumptions, and even quite complex devices have levels of current drain that are totally insignificant when they are operating at very low frequencies or are static. The current consumption increases as the operating frequency of the device is raised -- a factor which is often ignored. At high operating frequencies the power consumption of a CMOS device will not necessarily be any less than that of an equivalent TTL type. As few logic circuits have a number of devices with all of them continuously operating flat out, in practice CMOS circuits generally have vastly lower power consumptions than TTL equivalents.

Also, ordinary 4000 series CMOS integrated circuits will not operate at very high frequencies, with a typical maximum of about 5 MHz, and some of the more complex devices falling well short of even this modest figure. Another drawback of standard CMOS integrated circuits is their vulnerability to damage by static electricity. The early 'A' series devices were perhaps more susceptible to this type of damage than the current 'B' suffix devices with their greatly improved built-in protection circuits. The risk of damage due to static charges is one which has probably been somewhat exaggerated anyway, and having treated these devices just like non-MOS types for many years I have not 'zapped' one yet. Many others treat them with equal contempt without any difficulties arising either.

Apart from their low current consumption, other advantages of standard CMOS devices are their relatively high fanout (each output can drive some fifty inputs), their wide operating voltage range (3 to 18 volts for the 'B' series devices), and extremely good immunity to noise on the supply rails. An important point to bear in mind is that the high fanout figure is achieved by these devices having a very high input impedance, and their maximum output current is, in general, comparatively low. Apart from possible problems in driving medium and high current loads such as light emitting diodes and relay coils, this means that CMOS devices have very limited fanout when driving most other types of logic device. In fact a normal CMOS output can not even be guaranteed to drive a single standard TTL input, and in most cases will fail to do so.

LS TTL

The LS (low-power Schottky) logic family is almost certainly the most popular at present, having effectively ousted the ordinary 7400 TTL range and established themselves as the new standard. They use Schottky diodes to prevent transistors at key points in the devices from being driven into saturation, and this enables improved switching speed to be obtained for a given operating current. The standard Schottky (74S00 series) devices have characteristics that are very similar to the standard TTL devices, but with a maximum operating frequency that is some three to four times higher. The low-power devices take the alternative path of having a similar speed performance to the standard devices, but with a much lower power consumption. In fact 74LS00 series devices are generally a little faster than their 7400 equivalents, but with only about one-fifth of the current consumption. This, coupled with their quite low cost, has made low-power Schottky devices an attractive proposition to circuit designers, and it is easy to see why they have become so popular.

There are other Schottky TTL logic families, and in particular the 74AS00 (advanced Schottky) and 74ALS00 (advanced low power Schottky) ranges. The advanced Schottky types are intended as an alternative to the standard Schottky types, but offering somewhat higher speed for about the same current consumption. The advanced low-power type are intended to be an alternative to the standard low-power type, and offer somewhat increased operating speed at only about half the power drain. Although these looked set to replace the 74LS00 range at one time, they have not achieved this so far, and look unlikely to do so now. More recent 'improved' families look likely to render them obsolete before they have a chance to really establish themselves.

HC CMOS

Most of the recent advances in logic device technology have involved CMOS components. However, these have been refined to the point where they are no longer restricted to low speed applications, and many modern CMOS devices are intended to be equivalents to TTL rather than 4000 series CMOS types. The original TTL look-alike CMOS devices were in the 74C00 range, and these were just standard CMOS devices with identical pinouts to the 7400 range devices they were imitating. They were really just intended to make it easier for designers who were familiar with TTL logic devices to use CMOS types, and they were not a technical advance over the 4000 series CMOS integrated circuits.

The same is certainly not true of the current 7400 style CMOS devices. The first of these was the 74HC00 (high-speed CMOS) range which offer a maximum operating frequency of around 60 MHz — nearly double that of standard TTL types. The 74HC00 components retain the high input impedance associated with ordinary CMOS types, but they have higher maximum drive currents which are closer to those offered by the various TTL ranges, although not quite equal to them. This gives a massive fanout capability when high-speed CMOS devices are used to drive other CMOS devices, and gives a respectable fanout figure when they are used to drive TTL inputs.

One important difference between 74HC00 range integrated circuits and conventional CMOS types is that they have a more restricted operating voltage range of 2 to 6 volts. This is still vastly better than most other TTL logic families, and the excellent supply noise immunity associated with CMOS logic devices is largely retained by the 74HC00 family. It is useful to bear in mind that there are 74HC equivalents to many 4000 series components, and not just devices from the 7400 range. For example, the 74HC73 is the high-speed CMOS version of the TTL 7473, and the 74HC4017 is high-speed CMOS version of the CMOS 4017BE. A point in favour of CMOS devices which is often overlooked is their wide operating temperature range of −40 to +85 degrees Centigrade, as opposed to a 0 to 70 degree Centigrade operating temperature range for ordinary consumer grade TTL devices (there are superior grade 5400 series TTL devices, but these are not available to non-industrial users). The high-speed CMOS devices fully retain this wider operating temperature range.

There are so-called "unbuffered" versions of ordinary CMOS devices, and these are primarily intended for circuits that use the devices in a pseudo-linear fashion (oscillators for example). There are also unbuffered versions of a few 74HC00 devices, and these have 74HCU00 type numbers. The unbuffered versions of ordinary CMOS devices have 4000UBE type numbers incidentally.

Another variation on the 74HC00 range is the 74HCT00 series. Whereas the standard high-speed CMOS range have input switching levels that are virtually the same as ordinary CMOS devices, the 74HCT00 range have input switching levels that are compatible with the 74LS00 series of devices. The 74HCT00 range is intended for use where high-speed CMOS devices are to be mixed with ordinary 74LS00 (or similar) TTL devices. Apart from the input switching levels their performance is very similar to the standard 74HC00 range, but there acceptable supply voltage range is more restricted at 4.5 to 5.5 volts, and of more significance, the supply noise immunity is not as good.

FACT

There are actually even more advanced CMOS logic devices in the form of the FACT (Fairchild Advanced CMOS Technology) devices. These have current consumptions that are comparable with the high-speed CMOS types, but they achieve something like double the operating speed, and also have much higher output current capability. Again there are types with ordinary CMOS switching levels (the 74AC00 range) and the fully TTL compatible types (the 74ACT00 series). Both types have a 2 to 6 volt supply voltage range. At the time of writing this, there are few FACT devices available, and amateur users could find it difficult to actually get hold of those that are currently manufactured. However, these devices seem likely to be more readily available in the future.

The Field

The above does not cover all the logic families that are currently available; but the others are relatively little used. These include the 74H00 range, which is a high speed but high current consumption type. There is also the FAST (Fast Advanced Schottky TTL) range, which is a faster and lower current consumption equivalent to the 74S00 series. There was at one time a low power TTL range (the 74L00 series), but their low power was reflected in their low operating speed, and these seem to have become obsolete (presumably having been overtaken by the standard CMOS devices). Where very high speed is needed ECL (emitter coupled logic) devices are the normal choice, but these feature little in home constructor designs. They have very high performance figures, but are quite costly, require dual supply rails, and have no pin for pin equivalents to either the 7400 or 4000 ranges of logic devices (which with their dual supply requirement would be impossible).

Mixing

Choosing the most suitable logic family for a given application is a matter of first checking to determine which ones are fast enough, and then choosing a good compromise between current consumption and cost. Generally 4000 series CMOS devices are best suited to low frequency applications while 74LS00 still offer the best compromise at higher frequencies. Resorting to the more exotic devices is generally only justified if very high speed operation or a combination of high speed and low current drain is essential. Of course, in due course the cost of 'improved' devices is likely to fall, making them more practical and probably rendering some of the earlier ranges obsolete.

Table 1 gives basic details of the more common logic families. As explained previously, the data it contains is in some cases a generalization and may not be totally correct for every device in the range. Gaps in the table indicate that searches of data books failed to turn up the relevant information, but the table is largely complete. This should aid selection of suitable devices, and when mixing logic families it is also a useful guide as to what will drive what, and how many it will drive. In general it is best to avoid any mixing of this type, and where possible faulty devices should be replaced with a device of exactly the same type rather than an equivalent from another logic family. Mixing of logic families is, of course, justifiable when the faulty device has become obsolete and there are supply difficulties with the correct device. It is also a common and sensible ploy to use high speed devices only in parts of the circuit that require them, with slower (and compatible) devices in the rest of the circuit.

TABLE 1

	Std TTL	LS TTL	ALS TTL	STTL
Supply Voltage	5V (± 5%)	5V (± 5%)	5V (± 10%)	5V (± 10%)
DC Fanout	40	20	20	50
Maximum Low Input	0.8V	0.8V	0.8V	0.8V
Minimum High Input	2V	2V	2V	2V
Maximum Low Output	0.4V	0.5V	0.5V	0.5V
Minimum High Output	2.4V	2.7V	2.7V	2.7V
DC Noise Margin (L/H)	0.3/0.7	0.3/0.7	0.4/0.7	0.3/0.7
Input Current (L/H)	40/1600 μA	20/400 μA	20/200 μA	–
Output Current (L/H)	16/0.4 mA	8/0.4 mA	8/0.4 mA	20/-
Temp. Range	0–70°C	0–70°C	0–70°C	0–70°C
Typical Maximum Frequency	35MHz	40MHz	70MHz	120MHz
Relative Power Dissipation	1	0.2	0.1	1

	Std CMOS	74HC	74HCT	FACT
Supply Voltage	3 to 18V	2 to 6V	5V (± 10%)	2 to 6V
DC Fanout	1	10	10	60
Maximum Low Input	1.5V	0.9V	0.8V	1.35V
Minimum High Input	3.5V	3.15V	2V	3.15V
Maximum Low Output	0.05V	0.1V	0.1V	0.1V
Minimum High Output	4.95V	4.9V	4.9V	4.9V
DC Noise Margin (L/H)	1.45/ 1.45	0.8/ 1.25	–/–	1.25/ 1.25
Input Current (L/H)	0.3/0.3 μA	1/1 μA	1/1 μA	1/1 μA
Output Current (L/H)	2.1/ 0.45 mA	4/4 mA	4/4 mA	24/24 mA
Temperature Range	–40 to +85°C	–40 to +85°C	–40 to +85°C	–40 to +85°C
Typical Maximum Frequency	5MHz	40MHz	40MHz	125MHz
Relative Power Dissipation	0.002	0.002	0.002	–

Note that the fanout figures are given in terms of LS TTL inputs. The CMOS devices mostly have quite wide operating voltage ranges, but the quoted input/output currents and voltages are for a 5-volt supply. The relative power dissipation figures are only a very rough guide, and assume that the devices are used at a low to medium frequency, and used intermittently at a high frequency. In general, the relative performance of 'improved' devices degrades as the input frequency is increased (especially the CMOS types). Most of the figures are generalisations and are for guidance only. For precise details of a given device the relevant data sheet or data book should be consulted.

Pinouts

A complete set of CMOS and TTL pinout diagrams would fill several books of this size, but the accompanying diagrams provide pinout details for most of the devices that are commonly encountered in home constructor designs, and these should prove to be useful for reference purposes.

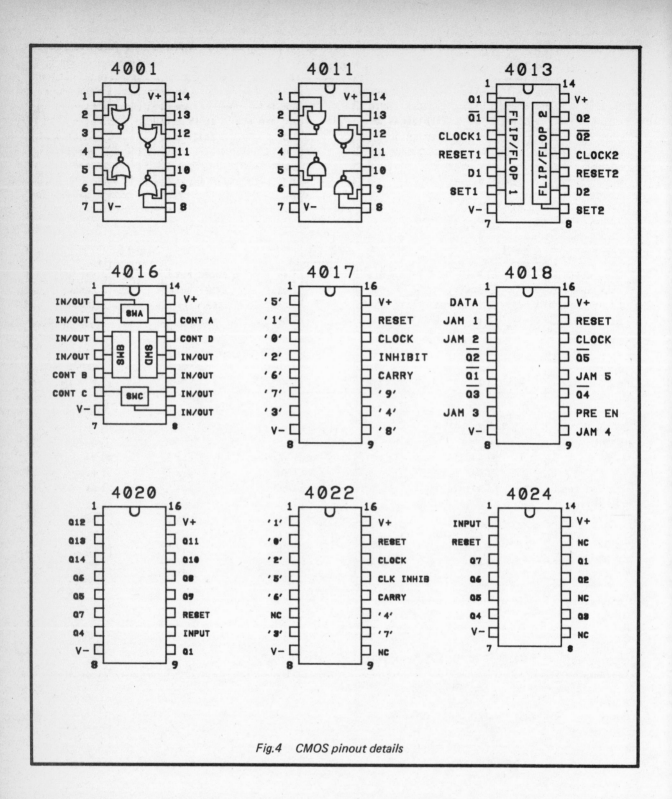

Fig.4   CMOS pinout details

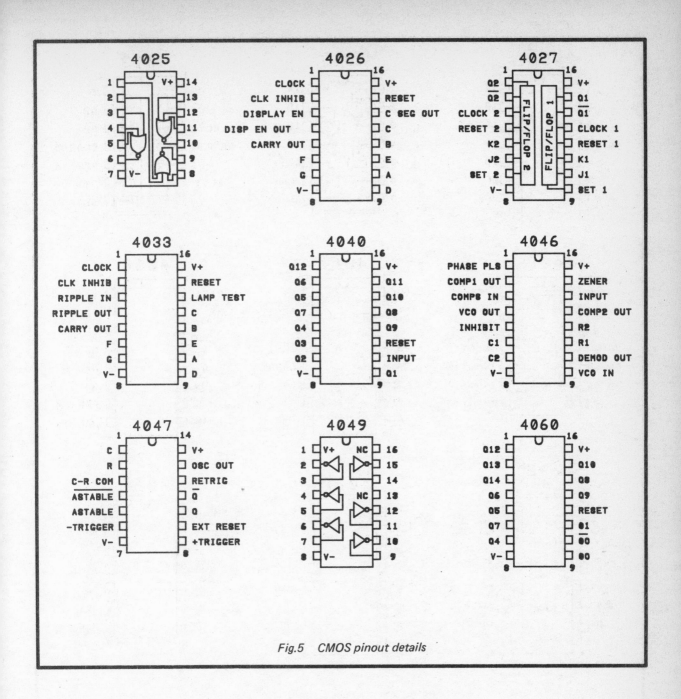

Fig.5   CMOS pinout details

11

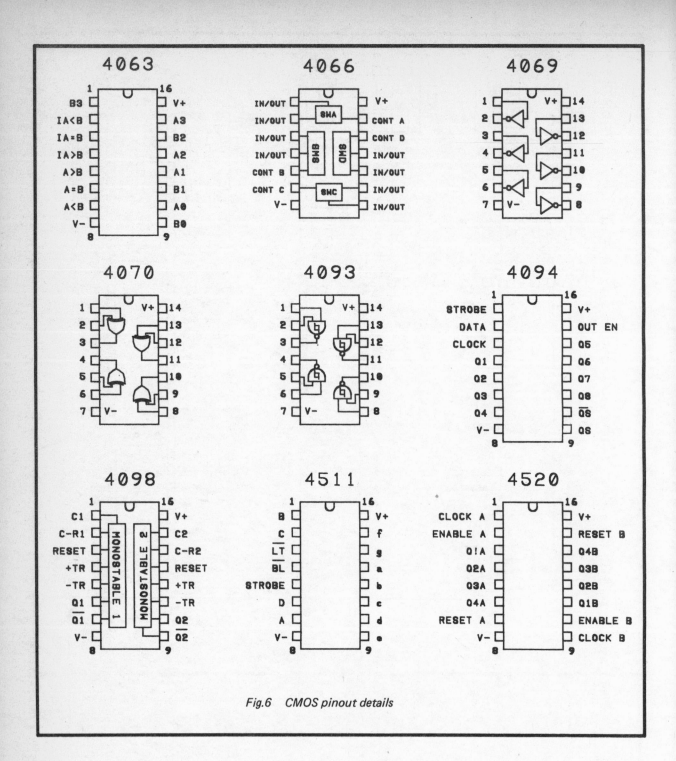

Fig.6   CMOS pinout details

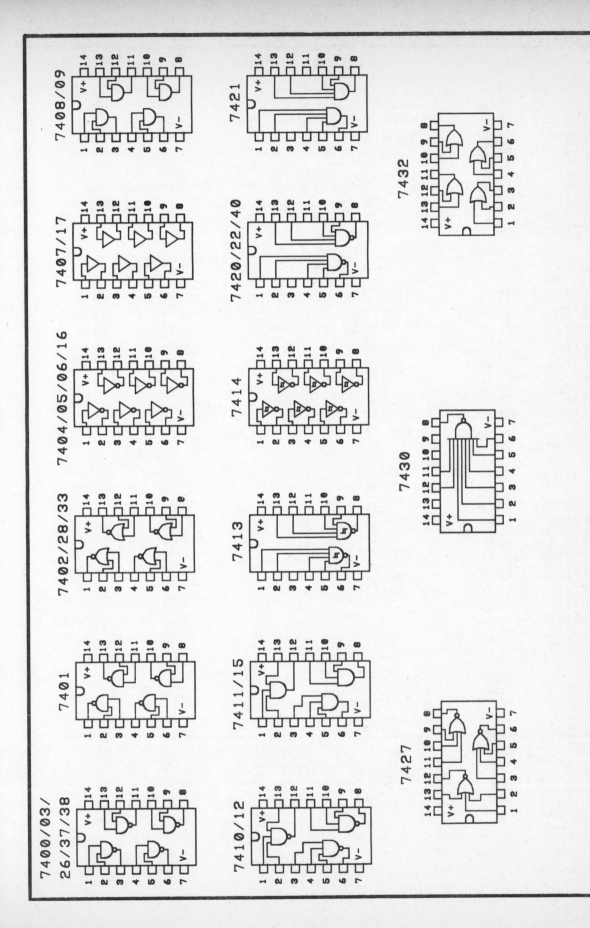

Fig.7   Pinout details for TTL gates

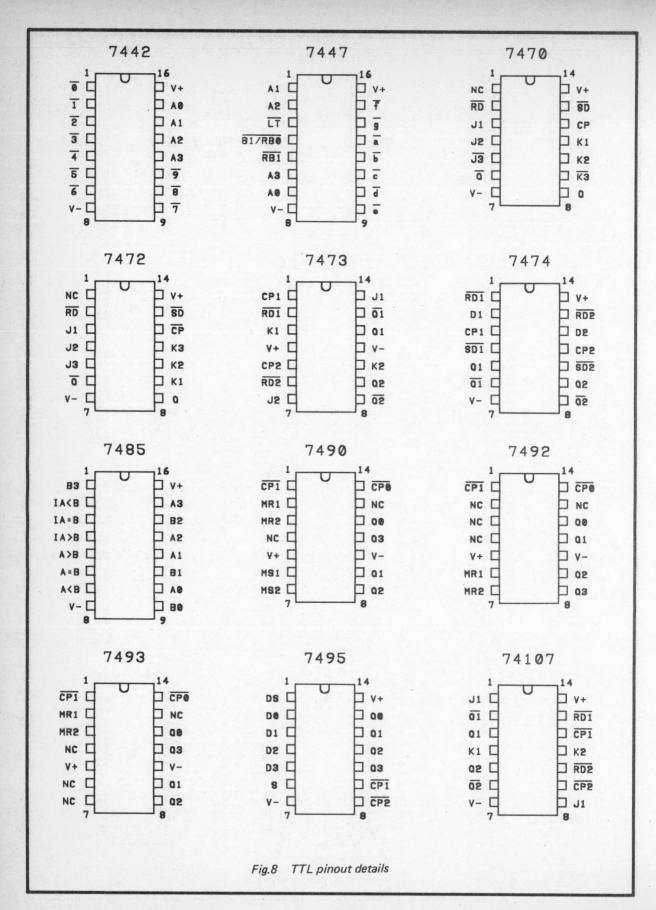

Fig.8   TTL pinout details

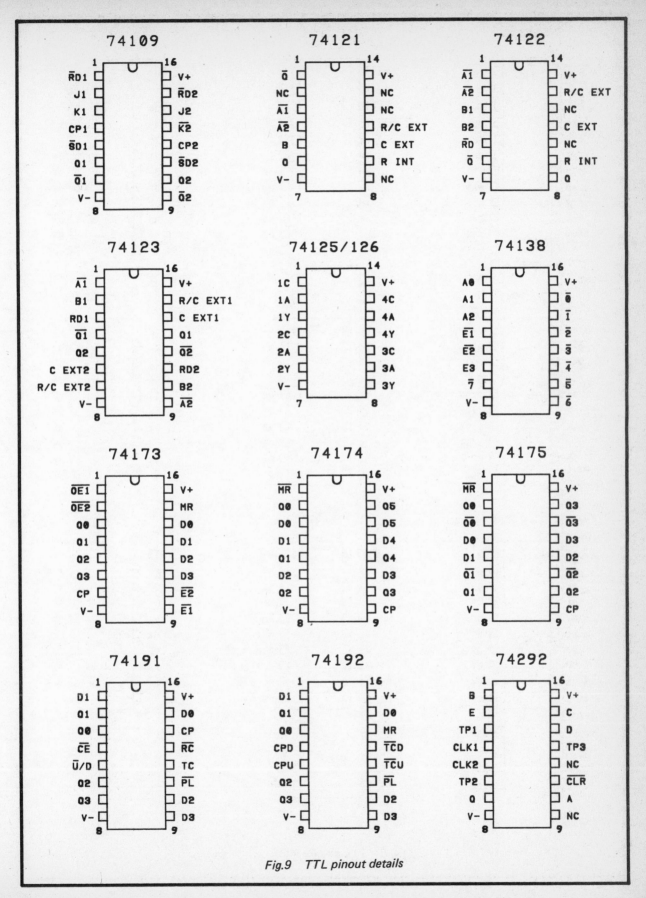

Fig.9   TTL pinout details

15

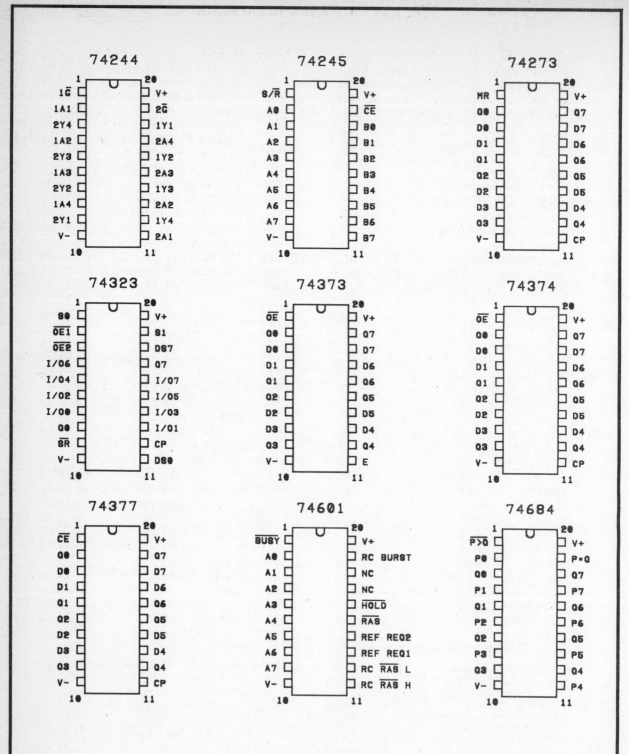

Fig. 10 Pinout details for some 20 pin TTL devices

TTL ICs FUNCTION AND PACKAGE

The following list covers TTL devices, and gives both the function and package type of each device that is listed. This should be useful when trying to find the function of a particular device. The smaller lists after the main one are helpful when looking for a device that has the required function. Not all TTL devices are included, but most of those that are readily available to non-professional users are listed here.

Device	Function	Package
7400	Quad 2 input NAND gate	14 pin DIL
7401	Quad 2 input NAND gate (open collector)	14 pin DIL
7402	Quad 2 input NOR gate	14 pin DIL
7403	Quad 2 input NAND gate (open collector)	14 pin DIL
7404	Hex inverter	14 pin DIL
7405	Hex inverter (open collector)	14 pin DIL
7406	Hex inverter/buffer (open collector)	14 pin DIL
7407	Hex buffer	14 pin DIL
7408	Quad 2 input AND gate	14 pin DIL
7409	Quad 2 input AND gate (open collector)	14 pin DIL
7410	Triple 3 input NAND gate	14 pin DIL
7411	Triple 3 input AND gate	14 pin DIL
7412	Triple 3 input NAND gate (open collector)	14 pin DIL
7413	Dual 4 input NAND (Schmitt Trigger)	14 pin DIL
7414	Hex Schmitt Trigger	14 pin DIL
7515	Triple 3 input AND gate (open collector)	14 pin DIL
7516	Hex inverter/buffer (open collector)	14 pin DIL
7417	Hex buffer (open collector)	14 pin DIL
7420	Dual 4 input NAND gate	14 pin DIL
7421	Dual 4 input AND gate	14 pin DIL
7422	Dual 4 input NAND gate (open collector)	14 pin DIL
7425	Dual 4 input NOR gate (with strobe)	14 pin DIL
7426	Quad 2 input NAND gate (open collector)	14 pin DIL
7427	Triple 3 input NOR gate	14 pin DIL
7428	Quad 2 input NOR buffer	14 pin DIL
7430	8 input NAND gate	14 pin DIL
7432	Quad 2 input OR gate	14 pin DIL
7433	Quad 2 input NOR buffer (open collector)	14 pin DIL
7437	Quad 2 input NAND buffer (open collector)	14 pin DIL
7438	Quad 2 input AND buffer (open collector)	14 pin DIL
7440	Dual 4 input NAND buffer	14 pin DIL
7442	BCD to decimal decoder (1 of 10)	16 pin DIL

Device	Function	Package
7447	BCD to 7 segment decoder/driver	16 pin DIL
7448	BCD to 7 segment decoder/driver	16 pin DIL
7451	Complex AND/OR/invert gate	14 pin DIL
7454	Complex AND/OR/invert gate	14 pin DIL
7470	JK edge triggered flip/flop	14 pin DIL
7472	JK pulse triggered flip/flop	14 pin DIL
7473	Dual JK flip/flop	14 pin DIL
7474	Dual D type flip/flop	14 pin DIL
7475	Dual 2 bit transparent latch	16 pin DIL
7476	Dual JK flip/flop	16 pin DIL
7481	16 bit RAM	14 pin DIL
7483	4 bit full adder	16 pin DIL
7485	4 bit magnitude comparator	16 pin DIL
7486	Quad 2 input XOR gate	14 pin DIL
7489	64 bit RAM	16 pin DIL
7490	Decade counter	14 pin DIL
7491	8 bit shift register	14 pin DIL
7492	Divide by 12 counter	14 pin DIL
7493	4 bit binary ripple counter	14 pin DIL
7495	4 bit shift register	14 pin DIL
7496	5 bit shift register	16 pin DIL
74107	Dual JK flip/flop	14 pin DIL
74109	Dual JK flip/flop	16 pin DIL
74112	Dual JK flip/flop	16 pin DIL
74113	Dual JK flip/flop	14 pin DIL
74118	Hex set/reset latch	16 pin DIL
74121	Monostable	14 pin DIL
74122	Retriggerable Monostable	14 pin DIL
74123	Dual retriggerable monostable	16 pin DIL
74125	Quad 3 state buffer	14 pin DIL
74126	Quad 3 state buffer	14 pin DIL
74132	Quad 2 input NAND Schmitt Trigger	14 pin DIL
74136	Quad 2 input XOR gate (open collector)	14 pin DIL
74137	3 to 8 line decoder	16 pin DIL
74138	3 to 8 line decoder	16 pin DIL
74139	Dual 1 of 4 decoder/demultiplexer	16 pin DIL
74141	BCD to decimal decoder/driver	16 pin DIL
74145	BCD to decimal decoder (open collector)	16 pin DIL
74150	16 input Multiplexer	24 pin DIL
74151	8 input Multiplexer	16 pin DIL
74153	Dual 4 to 1 Multiplexer	16 pin DIL
74154	1 of 16 decoder/demultiplexer	24 pin DIL
74155	Dual 2 to 4 line decoder	16 pin DIL
74156	Dual 2 to 4 line decoder (open collector)	16 pin DIL
74157	Quad 2 input data selector (non-inverted)	16 pin DIL
74158	Quad 2 input data selector (inverted)	16 pin DIL
74160	4 bit decade counter	16 pin DIL

Device	Function	Package
74161	4 bit binary counter	16 pin DIL
74162	4 bit decade counter (sync)	16 pin DIL
74163	4 bit binary counter (sync)	16 pin DIL
74164	8 bit ser. in/par. out shift register	14 pin DIL
74165	8 bit ser./par. in/ser. out shift register	16 pin DIL
74166	8 bit ser./par. in/ser. out shift register	16 pin DIL
74168	4 bit up/down synchronous decade counter	16 pin DIL
74169	4 bit up/down synchronous binary counter	16 pin DIL
74170	4 x 4 register file	16 pin DIL
74173	Quad D type flip/flop (3 state outputs)	16 pin DIL
74174	Hex D type flip/flop	16 pin DIL
74175	Quad D type flip/flop	16 pin DIL
74181	4 bit ALU	24 pin DIL
74190	Presettable BCD decade up/down counter	16 pin DIL
74191	Presettable 4 bit binary up/down counter	16 pin DIL
74192	Presettable BCD decade up/down counter	16 pin DIL
74193	Presettable 4 bit binary up/down counter	16 pin DIL
74194	4 bit bidirectional universal shift register	16 pin DIL
74195	4 bit parallel access shift register	16 pin DIL
74196	Presettable decade ripple counter	14 pin DIL
74197	Presettable 4 bit binary ripple counter	14 pin DIL
74221	Dual monostable multivibrator	16 pin DIL
74237	3 to 8 line decoder	16 pin DIL
74238	3 to 8 line decoder	16 pin DIL
74240	Octal inverter/buffer (3 state outputs)	20 pin DIL
74241	Octal buffer (3 state outputs)	20 pin DIL
74242	Quad inverting transceiver (3 state)	14 pin DIL
74243	Quad transceiver (3 state outputs)	14 pin DIL
74244	Octal buffer (3 state outputs)	20 pin DIL
74245	Octal transceiver (3 state outputs)	20 pin DIL
74251	8 input multiplexer (3 state outputs)	16 pin DIL
74253	Dual 4 input multiplexer (3 state outputs)	16 pin DIL
74257	Quad 2 to 1 line data selector (3 state outputs, non-inverting)	16 pin DIL
74258	Quad 2 to 1 line data selector (3 state outputs, inverting)	16 pin DIL
74259	8 bit addressable latch	16 pin DIL
74260	Dual 5 input NOR gate	16 pin DIL
74261	Multiplex decoder	14 pin DIL
74266	Quad 2 input XNOR gate (open collector)	14 pin DIL

Device	Function	Package
74273	Octal D type flip/flop	20 pin DIL
74279	Quad set/reset latch	16 pin DIL
74283	4 bit full adder with fast carry	16 pin DIL
74290	Decade counter	14 pin DIL
74292	Programmable divider/timer	16 pin DIL
74293	4 bit binary ripple counter	14 pin DIL
74297	Digital phase locked loop filter	16 pin DIL
74298	Quad 2 port register, true & comp outputs	16 pin DIL
74323	8 bit universal shift/storage register	20 pin DIL
74365	Hex buffer, 3 state, gated enable inputs	16 pin DIL
74366	Hex inverter, 3 state, gated enable inputs	16 pin DIL
74367	Hex buffer, 3 state, enable inputs	16 pin DIL
74368	Hex inverter, 3 state, enable inputs	16 pin DIL
74373	Octal transparent latch, 3 state outputs	20 pin DIL
74374	Octal D type flip/flop, 3 state outputs	20 pin DIL
74377	Octal D type flip/flop with clock enable	20 pin DIL
74378	Hex D type flip/flop with clock enable	16 pin DIL
74379	Quad D type flip/flop with clock enable	16 pin DIL
74390	Dual decade ripple counter	16 pin DIL
74393	Dual 4 bit binary ripple counter	14 pin DIL
74395	4 bit cascadable shift register, 3 state	16 pin DIL
74399	Quad 2 port register, single rail output	16 pin DIL
74490	Decade counter	16 pin DIL
74534	Octal D type flip/flop	20 pin DIL
74601	Dynamic RAM Refresh controller (64k)	20 pin DIL
74604	Octal 2 input multiplexed latch, 3 state	28 pin DIL
74629	Voltage controlled oscillator	16 pin DIL
74670	4 x 4 register file, 3 state	16 pin DIL
74684	8 bit magnitude comparator	20 pin DIL

Gates

AND

7408	Quad 2 input	
7409	Quad 2 input (open collector)	
7411	Triple 3 input	
7415	Triple 3 input (open collector)	
7421	Dual 4 input	

NAND

7400	Quad 2 input	
7401	Quad 2 input (open collector)	
7403	Quad 2 input (open collector)	
7410	Triple 3 input	
7420	Dual 4 input	

Device	Function
7422	Dual 4 input (open collector)
7426	Quad 2 input
7430	Single 8 input
7437	Quad 2 input buffer
7438	Quad 2 input buffer (open collector)
74132	Quad 2 input (Schmitt Trigger)

OR

Device	Function
7432	Quad 2 input

NOR

Device	Function
7402	Quad 2 input
7425	Dual 4 input (with strobe)
7427	Triple 3 input
7428	Quad 2 input buffer
7433	Quad 2 input buffer
74260	Dual 5 input

XOR/XNOR

Device	Function
7486	Quad 2 input XOR
74136	Quad 2 input XOR (open collector)
74266	Quad 2 input XNOR

Buffers

Device	Function
7404	Hex inverter
7405	Hex inverter (open collector)
7406	Hex inverter (open collector)
7407	Hex (open collector)
7414	Hex inverter (Schmitt Trigger)
7416	Hex inverter (open collector)
7417	Hex (open collector)
74125	Quad 3 state (low enable)
74126	Quad 3 state (high enable)
74365	Hex 3 state
74366	Hex inverting 3 state
74367	Hex 3 state
74368	Hex 3 state inverting

Flip/Flops

Device	Function
7470	Single JK (positive edge triggered)
7472	Single JK (master slave)
7473	Dual JK with clear
7474	Dual D type (edge triggered)
7475	4 bit bistable latch
7476	Dual JK with clear and preset
74107	Dual JK with clear
74109	Dual JK (positive edge triggered)
74112	Dual JK (negative edge triggered)
74118	Hex set/reset latch
74174	Hex D type
74175	Quad D type
74273	Octal D type
74373	Octal D type transparent latch
74374	Octal D type 3 state
74377	Octal D type (common enable)
74534	Octal D type 3 state (inverting)

Device	Function
Shift Registers	
7495	4 bit shift register
7496	5 bit shift register
74164	8 bit shift register
74165	8 bit shift register
74166	8 bit shift register
74170	4 x 4 register file
74194	4 bit shift register
74195	4 bit parallel shift register
74395	4 bit cascadable shift register

Device	Function
Counters	
7490	Decade counter
7492	Divide by 12 counter
7493	4 bit binary counter
74160	4 bit decade counter
74161	4 bit binary counter
74162	4 bit decade counter (synchronous)
74163	4 bit binary counter (synchronous)
74169	4 bit binary counter
74190	BCD counter
74191	Binary counter
74192	BCD dual clock counter
74193	Binary dual clock counter
74196	Presettable decade counter
74197	Presettable binary counter
74390	Dual decade counter
74490	Decade counter

Device	Function
Decoders/Drivers	
7442	BCD to decimal decoder
7447	BCD to 7 segment decoder
7448	BCD to 7 segment decoder
74137	3 to 8 line decoder
74138	3 to 8 line decoder
74139	Dual 2 to 4 line decoder
74141	BCD to decimal decoder
74145	BCD to decimal decoder
74150	1 of 16 data selector
74151	1 of 8 data selector
74153	Dual 4 to 1 line data selector
74154	4 to 16 line decoder
74155	Dual 2 to 4 line
74156	Dual 2 to 4 line (open collector)
74157	Quad 2 to 1 line data selector
74158	Quad 2 to 1 line data selector
74237	3 to 8 line decoder
74238	3 to 8 line decoder
74251	Data selector
74257	Quad data selector

Device	Function
Miscellaneous	
7485	4 bit magnitude comparator
74121	Monostable
74122	Retriggerable monostable
74123	Dual retriggerable monostable
74245	Octal transceiver
74629	Dual voltage controlled oscillator
74684	8 bit magnitude comparator

CMOS ICs FUNCTION AND PACKAGE

These lists are the CMOS equivalents to the TTL ones provided previously. Again, the entire range of devices is not covered, but most of those that are available to the electronics hobbyist are included here.

Device	Function	Package
4000	Dual 3 input NOR gate and inverter	14 pin DIL
4001	Quad 2 input NOR gate	14 pin DIL
4002	Dual 4 input NOR gate	14 pin DIL
4006	18 stage static shift register	14 pin DIL
4007	Dual complementary pair plus inverter	14 pin DIL
4008	4 bit full adder	14 pin DIL
4009	Hex inverting buffer	14 pin DIL
4010	Hex buffer	14 pin DIL
4011	Quad 2 input NAND gate	14 pin DIL
4012	Dual 4 input NAND gate	14 pin DIL
4013	Dual D type flip/flop	14 pin DIL
4014	8 bit shift register	16 pin DIL
4015	8 bit shift register	16 pin DIL
4016	Quad SPST analogue switch	14 pin DIL
4017	One of ten decoder	16 pin DIL
4018	Presettable BCD counter	16 pin DIL
4019	Quad AND/OR select gate	16 pin DIL
4020	14 stage binary ripple counter	16 pin DIL
4021	8 stage static shift register	16 pin DIL
4022	Divide by 8 and 1 of 8 decoder	16 pin DIL
4023	Triple 3 input NAND gate	14 pin DIL
4024	7 stage binary ripple counter	14 pin DIL
4025	Triple 3 input NOR gate	14 pin DIL
4026	Decade counter/7 segment driver	16 pin DIL
4027	Dual JK master slave flip/flop	16 pin DIL
4028	BCD to decimal decoder	16 pin DIL
4029	Presettable up/down counter	16 pin DIL
4030	Quad 2 input XOR gate	14 pin DIL
4033	Decade counter/7 segment driver	16 pin DIL
4035	4 stage shift register	16 pin DIL
4040	12 stage binary counter	16 pin DIL
4041	Quad buffer	14 pin DIL
4042	Quad clocked D latch	16 pin DIL
4043	Quad NOR R/S latch (3 state)	16 pin DIL
4044	Quad NAND latch (3 state)	16 pin DIL
4046	Micro-power phase locked loop	16 pin DIL
4047	Astable/monostable	14 pin DIL
4049	Hex inverting buffer	16 pin DIL
4050	Hex buffer	16 pin DIL
4051	8 way 1 pole analogue switch	16 pin DIL
4052	Dual 4 way 1 pole analogue switch	16 pin DIL
4053	3 way 2 pole analogue switch	16 pin DIL
4056	BCD to 7 segment decoder (LCD)	16 pin DIL

Device	Function	Package
4060	Oscillator and 14 stage binary counter	16 pin DIL
4063	4 bit magnitude comparator	16 pin DIL
4066	Quad SPST analogue switch	14 pin DIL
4067	16 way 1 pole analogue switch	24 pin DIL
4068	8 input AND/NAND gate	14 pin DIL
4069	Hex inverter	14 pin DIL
4070	Quad 2 input XOR gate	14 pin DIL
4071	Quad 2 input OR gate	14 pin DIL
4072	Dual 4 input OR gate	14 pin DIL
4073	Triple 3 input AND gate	14 pin DIL
4075	Triple 3 input OR gate	14 pin DIL
4076	4 bit D type register	16 pin DIL
4077	Quad 2 input XNOR gate	14 pin DIL
4078	8 input NOR gate	14 pin DIL
4081	Quad 2 input AND gate	14 pin DIL
4082	Dual 4 input AND gate	14 pin DIL
4093	Quad 2 input NAND Schmitt Trigger	14 pin DIL
4094	8 stage shift register	16 pin DIL
4098	Dual monostable	16 pin DIL
4099	8 bit addressable latch	16 pin DIL
40103	8 stage counter	16 pin DIL
40105	FIFO register	16 pin DIL
40106	Hex Schmitt Trigger	14 pin DIL
40107	Dual 2 input NAND buffer	8 pin DIL
40108	4 x 4 multiport register	24 pin DIL
40109	Quad voltage shifter	16 pin DIL
40110	Decade up/down counter/7 segment driver	16 pin DIL
40174	Hex D type flip/flop	16 pin DIL
40181	4 bit logic unit	24 pin DIL
40182	Look ahead carry generator	16 pin DIL
40257	Quad 2 to 1 line data selector	16 pin DIL
4416	Quad SPST analogue switch	14 pin DIL
4419	Keyboard to binary encoder	16 pin DIL
4502	Strobed hex inverter	16 pin DIL
4503	Hex buffer (3 state)	16 pin DIL
4508	Dual 4 bit latch	24 pin DIL
4510	BCD presettable counter	16 pin DIL
4511	BCD 7 segment decoder driver	16 pin DIL
4512	8 channel data selector	16 pin DIL
4514	4 to 16 line decoder	24 pin DIL
4515	4 to 16 line decoder	24 pin DIL
4516	Presettable binary counter	16 pin DIL
4518	Dual BCD counter	16 pin DIL
4520	Dual binary counter	16 pin DIL
4526	4 bit binary counter	16 pin DIL
4528	Dual monostable	16 pin DIL
4532	8 bit priority encoder	16 pin DIL
4536	Programmable counter	16 pin DIL
4541	Programmable timer	14 pin DIL
4555	Dual binary to 1 of 4 decoder	16 pin DIL
45100	4 x 4 crosspoint switch	16 pin DIL

Device	Function

Gates

AND

4073	Triple 3 input
4081	Quad 2 input
4082	Dual 4 input

NAND

4011	Quad 2 input
4012	Dual 4 input
4023	Triple 3 input
4068	8 input
4093	Quad 2 input (Schmitt Trigger)

OR

4071	Quad 2 input
4072	Dual 4 input
4075	Triple 3 input

NOR

4001	Quad 2 input
4002	Dual 4 input
4025	Triple 3 input
4078	8 input

XOR/XNOR

4030	Quad 2 input XOR
4070	Quad 2 input XOR
4077	Quad 2 input XNOR

Buffers

4009	Hex inverting
4010	Hex
4041	Quad (true/complement)
4049	Hex inverting (high current)
4050	Hex (high current)
4069	Hex inverting
40106	Hex inverting (Schmitt Trigger)
40109	Quad (voltage shifter)
4502	Hex inverting (3 state)
4503	Hex (3 state)

Flip/Flops

4013	Dual D type
4027	Dual JK master slave
4042	Quad clocked D latch
4043	Quad 3 state NOR R/S latch
4044	Quad 3 state NAND R/S latch
4076	4 bit D type register
40108	4 x 4 multiport register
40174	Hex D type
4508	Dual 4 bit latch

Shift Registers

4006	18 bit shift register
4014	8 bit shift register
4015	8 bit shift register
4021	8 stage static shift register

Device	Function
4035	4 stage static shift register
4094	8 stage shift register
40105	FIFO register

Counters

4017	Divide by 10 (plus 1 of 10 decoder)
4018	Presettable BCD counter
4020	14 stage binary ripple counter
4022	Divide by 8 (plus 1 of 8 decoder)
4024	7 stage binary ripple counter
4026	Decade counter (7 segment driver)
4029	Presettable up/down counter
4033	Decade counter (7 segment driver)
4040	12 stage binary ripple counter
4060	14 stage binary counter (plus oscillator)
40103	8 stage counter
40110	Decade up/down counter (7 segment driver)
4510	Presettable counter
4516	Binary presettable counter
4518	Dual BCD counter
4520	Dual binary counter
4526	4 bit binary counter
4536	Programmable counter

Decoders Etc.

4017	1 of 10 decoder
4022	1 of 8 decoder
4026	Decade counter/7 segment decoder
4028	BCD to decimal decoder
4033	Decade counter/7 segment decoder
4051	8 channel analogue multiplexer
4052	Dual 4 channel analogue multiplexer
4053	Triple 2 channel multiplexer
4056	BCD to 7 segment decoder (LCD)
4067	16 channel analogue multiplexer
4419	Keyboard to binary encoder
4511	BCD to 7 segment decoder
4512	8 channel data selector
4514	4 to 16 line decoder
4515	4 to 16 line decoder
4532	8 bit priority encoder

Miscellaneous

4016	Quad SPST analogue switch
4046	Micro-power phase locked loop
4047	Monostable/Astable
4063	4 bit magnitude comparator
4066	Quad SPST analogue switch
4098	Dual monostable
40181	4 bit logic unit
4416	Quad SPDT analogue switch
4541	Programmable timer
45100	4 x 4 crosspoint switch

Power supplies are an aspect of electronics which looks deceptively simple, but there are a few traps awaiting anyone who treats this subject contemptuously. Mains power supply circuits are in two main categories; stabilised and non-stabilised types. Really a stabilised supply is just a non-stabilised type to which a voltage regulator circuit has been added, and so we will consider non-stabilised supplies first, and then progress the subject of voltage regulators.

Rectification

Most mains power supplies use a transformer for isolation and voltage step-down purposes, and this is the only type of supply that we will consider here. The output from the secondary winding of the transformer is, of course, an A.C. signal which must be rectified in order to produce a D.C. output. Rectification alone is not normally sufficient, as this gives a pulsing D.C. output, whereas most applications require a reasonably ripple-free D.C. supply. A large smoothing capacitor is connected across the output of the supply, and this charges up on output voltage peaks. The stored charge is fed to the load between peaks, and this gives the required smoothing action. A very large capacitor is needed in order to give a really low output ripple level, and in many cases the required value would be impractically large. It is common practice to get around this by using a stabiliser circuit to provide electronic smoothing and a very low noise level on the output, even if the regulation of the output voltage is not actually necessary.

The most simple form of power supply circuit is the half-wave type of Figure 11. With this circuit the rectifier conducts on peak positive excursions, but it blocks negative half cycles. This type of circuit is little used in practice as it is very inefficient. One reason for this is that the transformer is only supplying power for a brief period once per cycle, and it is heavily loaded during this period (causing its output

voltage to sag significantly). It is a common error to assume that because a transformer has a current rating of (say) 1 amp it can provide a rectified and smoothed D.C. output current of 1 amp. This is not usually the case, and the current rating of a transformer is its A.C. rating. The D.C. output current that can be obtained depends on the type of rectification used, and to some extent on the amount of smoothing. It is generally somewhat lower than the A.C. current rating of the transformer due to the pulsed fashion in which it is obtained. The half-wave rectifier is the least efficient type and it offers a maximum continuous D.C. output current equal to only about 28% of the transformer's A.C. current rating.

Another problem with this type of circuit is in smoothing the output sufficiently to give a reasonably low ripple level. With the transformer and rectifier circuit providing only a brief surge of current once per cycle this leaves a relatively long gap between pulses for the smoothing capacitor to fill in. This type of circuit is consequently little used in practice, although it is perfectly suitable where only low output currents are involved. The low efficiency is then of little importance, and a comparatively small smoothing capacitor is sufficient to give a well smoothed output.

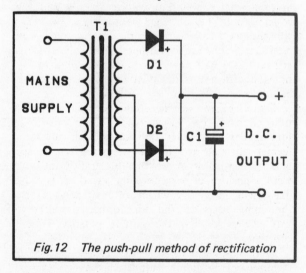

Fig.12   The push-pull method of rectification

Figure 12 shows the so-called push-pull type of rectifier circuit, and this is effectively two half-wave types operating in anti-phase. When D1 is fed with a positive half cycle from its winding on T1, D2 will be fed with a negative half cycle. When D2 is fed with a positive half cycle D1 is fed with a negative one. The key point here is that on each half cycle one or other of the rectifiers conducts and supplies power to the smoothing capacitor and the load across the output. This gives better efficiency and eases the problem of smoothing the output signal.

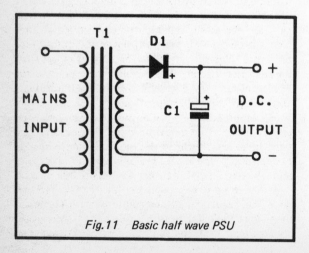

Fig.11   Basic half wave PSU

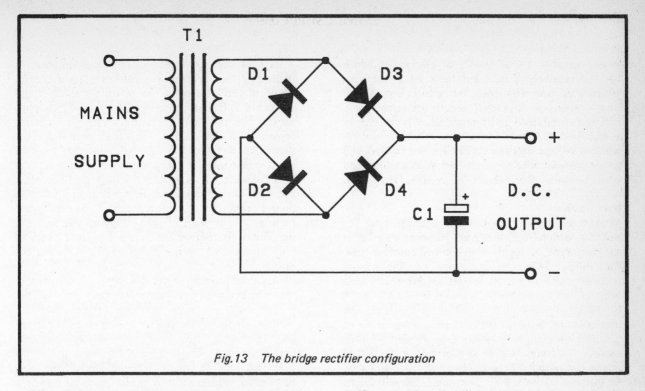

Fig.13   The bridge rectifier configuration

The maximum continuous output current is actually the same as the A.C. current rating of the transformer for this configuration, but this is not quite as good as it at first appears. It has to be borne in mind that the output voltage is only half that which would be obtained if the two secondary windings were to be used in series to drive a half-wave rectifier. The circuit is therefore nearly twice as efficient as a half-wave type, and not three to four times as efficient as might at first have appeared to be the case.

Figure 13 shows the bridge rectifier configuration, which is a full-wave type. The effect of the four diodes is to steer the output from the transformer through to the output with the correct polarity regardless of whether the transformer provides a positive or negative going signal. It is rather like having a switch which automatically reverses the connections to the transformer on alternate half cycles so that the output polarity remains constant.

In terms of efficiency, with a bridge rectifier the maximum continuous output current is approximately 62% of the transformer's current rating. In practical power supply designs it is not uncommon for transformers to be used somewhat beyond their theoretical maximum output current. This may be acceptable where the output will not be fully loaded continuously, but is a somewhat risky practice.

The theoretical output voltage of these circuits under zero loading is 1.42 times the A.C. voltage rating of the transformer. This ignores any voltage drop through the rectifier circuit, and with silicon rectifiers this will be in the region of 0.7 volts for the half-wave and push-pull circuits, and about 1.4 volts for the bridge rectifier type (where there is always two diodes in the signal path). In my experience the true unloaded output voltage is usually more like 1.5 times the transformer's secondary voltage rating, and is sometimes a little higher than this. The output voltage at full load is generally about equal to the voltage rating of the transformer. This obviously gives an enormous variation in output voltage with changes in loading, and the use of voltage stabilisation is often essential in applications where large variations in the load current will occur.

The most suitable value for the smoothing capacitor depends on the maximum output current and the acceptable ripple level. Often it is not possible to obtain really low ripple levels as the required smoothing capacitance would be unrealistically high, and it would also result in the diodes conducting for only a very short period of time, during which they would pass an excessively high current. From the time constant of the smoothing capacitor and output load resistance, plus the time between current pulses from the rectifier circuit, it is possible to calculate the ripple voltage. As a general rule of thumb though, about 2 μF per milliamp of output current gives a good compromise between output ripple and rectifier pulse current. The operating voltage of the capacitor must be at least equal to the off load output voltage of the supply, and should preferably be about 20% or more higher than this to leave a reasonable margin.

It has to be stressed that the high ripple level and poor load regulation of non-stabilised supplies makes them unsuitable for anything other than non-critical applications. Of course, many circuits (including some popular audio amplifier integrated circuit types for example) are designed to be able to cope with poor regulation and high ripple levels. It is often possible to obtain satisfactory results by doing this instead of resorting to a stabilised supply, with a substantial reduction in the cost of the overall circuit.

With supply circuits you should always bear in mind that the rectifiers have to withstand about double the output voltage during the half cycles when they are not conducting. This is because one terminal of the rectifier connects to the output and will be positive by an amount equal to the supply voltage, whereas the other terminal connects to the secondary winding and will be taken negative by a similar amount. Thus the rectifiers must have a P.I.V. (peak inverse voltage rating) that is something over double the output voltage.

Note that in order to reverse the polarity of the output voltage of these circuits it is merely necessary to change the polarity of the rectifiers (plus the smoothing capacitor, of course).

This table provides basic data on two widely available ranges of rectifier (the 1N4000 and 1N5400 series). These cover the vast majority of power supply applications, and only very high current or E.H.T. supplies will require anything more exotic. Details of the high current MR75X series are also included. For E.H.T. supplies a 'special' device such as the BY713 is required, but very high voltage supplies are something that only those with suitable experience should get involved with.

Type	PIV	Current	Max. V. Drop
1N4001	50V	1A	1.1V
1N4002	100V	1A	1.1V
1N4003	200V	1A	1.1V
1N4004	400V	1A	1.1V
1N4005	600V	1A	1.1V
1N4006	800V	1A	1.1V
1N4007	1000V	1A	1.1V
1N5400	50V	3A	1.1V
1N5401	100V	3A	1.1V
1N5402	200V	3A	1.1V
1N5404	400V	3A	1.1V
1N5406	600V	3A	1.1V
1N5407	800V	3A	1.1V
1N5408	1000V	3A	1.1V
MR752	200V	6A	1.1V
MR754	400V	6A	1.1V
MR756	600V	6A	1.1V
MR758	800V	6A	1.1V

Note that the voltage drop is at the maximum rated current of the device, and is a worse case figure not a typical one.

Most rectifiers have diode style encapsulations with a band around the body of the component to indicate the cathode (' + ') terminal. However, there are other styles, such as the stud-mounting types, and Figure 14 should help to clarify matters if you are faced with an unfamiliar type.

Regulators

Where the use of a regulator is unavoidable the first point is to ensure that the supply circuit which feeds it can provide an adequate loaded voltage. If a voltage regulator has a stabilised output potential of 5 volts, that is not to say that it will provide this output voltage with an input voltage as low as 5 volts. Regulator circuits have a 'drop-out' voltage, which is the minimum input potential needed to maintain the rated output voltage. This is typically about 2 to 3 volts more than the output voltage. Any ripple on the input to the regulator has to be taken into account, and the loaded output of the non-regulated supply should therefore be about 1 volt more than the drop-out voltage of the regulator. It is alright if the loaded non-stabilised supply potential is more than this, but it should not be substantially greater than is really necessary as this would unnecessarily increase the power dissipation in the regulator.

The most simple type of regulator is the zener shunt type which has the basic circuit configuration shown in Figure 15.

This is really only suitable for very low power applications as it is a type of circuit which is rather wasteful of power in most cases. Another point to bear in mind is that low voltage zener diodes (by which I mean types with an operating voltage of about 6.8 volts or less) are not generally very efficient, and will not give a well stabilised supply. With any zener diode it is possible to obtain much improved performance by feeding the device from a constant current generator. For applications that require really accurate voltages and very high regulation efficiency there are special voltage regulator devices (such as the ZN423) which operate like highly efficient zener diodes. They also offer very low temperature drift. Inclusion of the decoupling capacitor is important incidentally, as zener diodes generate quite strong noise spikes (and are sometimes used as noise generators), and these must obviously be filtered out in order to give a well smoothed and noise-free output.

The value of load resistor R1 is important, as this must always provide an adequate current flow to the output, but must not be so low in value that large amounts of power are wasted or the zener diode is burned out. The basic action of the circuit is for the zener to conduct more heavily if the load current decreases, or less heavily if it increases. This keeps the overall current drain virtually constant, and avoids significant variations in the output voltage due to loading variations. If the input voltage should increase or decrease for some reason, D1 conducts more or less heavily so that the voltage drop through R1 (more or less) changes by the same amount, and keeps the output voltage virtually constant.

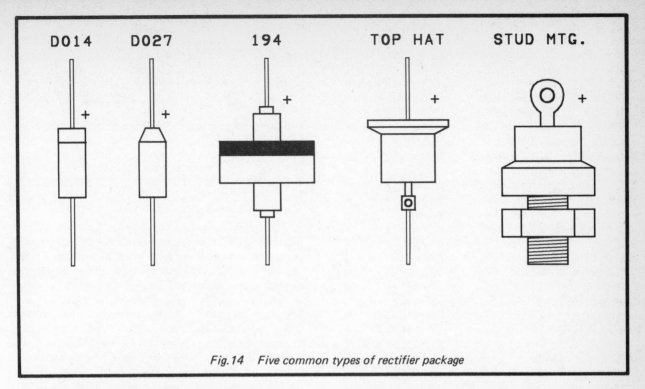

DO14   DO27   194   TOP HAT   STUD MTG.

Fig.14   Five common types of rectifier package

In order to calculate the value for R1 we must know the minimum input voltage, maximum output current, and the output voltage. The output voltage is deduct from the minimum input voltage to give the minimum voltage across R1. For the circuit to stand any chance of operating reasonably well this should be at least 1 volt, and preferably 2 or 3 volts. There must always be at least a small current flow through D1 for it to provide a stabilising action, and this current must be added to the output current. For small zener diodes a minimum current of just 2 or 3 milliamps is usually sufficient. The value for R1 is equal to the minimum voltage across this component divided by the total output current (including the zener current).

As a simple example, assume that the minimum input potential will be 8 volts, that the output voltage is 6.2 volts, and that the maximum output current is 7.5 milliamps. This gives a minimum voltage across R1 of 1.8 volts (8 − 6.2 = 1.8). Allowing 2.5 milliamps for the zener current, this gives a total output current of 10 milliamps (0.01 amps). The value for R1 is therefore equal to 1.8 volts divided by 0.01 amps, which gives an answer of 180 ohms. This is a preferred value, but in most cases the answer will not be exactly equal to a preferred value. It is then a matter of using the nearest preferred value below the calculated figure.

It is as well to calculate the power dissipated by R1 and D1 under worst case conditions to ensure that these will not be excessive for ordinary 250mW and 400mW components. If necessary higher power components can then be substituted. However, for medium and high power applications some form of series regulator is generally much more satisfactory.

At one time there were several readily available ranges of zener diodes covering a very wide voltage span. There are only two ranges of zener diode stocked by most component retailers these days, as detailed below:—

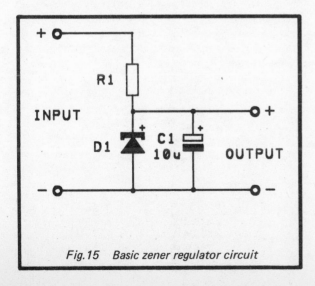

Fig.15   Basic zener regulator circuit

Voltage	400mW	1.3W
2.7V	BZY88C2V7	—
3V	BZY88C3V0	—
3.3V	BZY88C3V3	BZX61C3V3
3.6V	BZY88C3V6	BZX61C3V6
3.9V	BZY88C3V9	BZX61C3V9
4.3V	BZY88C4V3	BZX61C4V3

Continued overleaf

Voltage	400mW	1.3W
4.7V	BZY88C4V7	BZX61C4V7
5.6V	BZY88C5V6	BZX61C5V6
6.2V	BZY88C6V2	BZX61C6V2
6.8V	BZY88C6V8	BZX61C6V8
7.5V	BZY88C7V5	BZX61C7V5
8.2V	BZY88C8V2	BZX61C8V2
9.1V	BZY88C9V1	BZX61C9V1
10V	BZY88C10V	BZX61C10V
11V	BZY88C11V	BZC61C11V
12V	BZY88C12V	BZX61C12V
13V	BZY88C13V	BZX61C13V
15V	BZY88C15V	BZX61C15V
16V	BZY88C16V	BZX61C16V
18V	BZY88C18V	BZX61C18V
20V	BZY88C20V	BZX61C20V
24V	BZY88C24V	BZX61C24V
27V	BZY88C27V	BZX61C27V
30V	BZY88C30V	BZX61C30V
33V	BZY88C33V	BZX61C33V
36V	—	BZX61C36V
39V	—	BZX61C39V
43V	—	BZX61C43V
47V	—	BZX61C47V

Series Regulators

For most purposes ordinary three terminal mono-lithic voltage regulators are the most convenient type, and they are available in a range of popular voltages, in both positive and negative forms. They are used in the simple circuit configuration of Figure 16.

There is little that is likely to give any problems when using these devices, and they are very stable and reliable. However, to guarantee stability the two decoupling capacitors (C1 and C2) are positioned physically close to the voltage regulator. C1 and C2 should be ceramic types with values no less than the specified figure of 100nF. The circuit diagram is shown as a negative earth type, but for positive earth operation it is merely necessary to use a 79XX series device instead of a 78XX type (as in Figure 17).

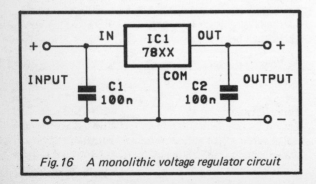

Fig.16   A monolithic voltage regulator circuit

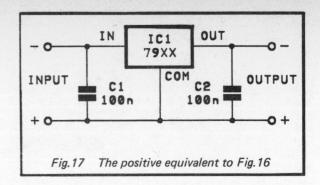

Fig.17   The positive equivalent to Fig.16

Performance figures vary somewhat from one particular device in these series to another, but in general the typical line regulation is better than 0.1%, the load regulation is about 0.25%, the ripple rejection is around 70dB, and the output noise voltage is in the region of 75 microvolts. This is more than adequate for most purposes, and is remarkably good when one takes into account the low cost of these components. They incorporate output short circuit protection in the form of fold-back current limiting. This simply means that in the event of a severe overload the output current is not merely prevented from exceeding a figure much in excess of the maximum rating of the component, but is actually reduced substantially as the loading on the output is increased. This reduces the risk of damage to the circuit powered by the supply unit, and it also helps to keep down the power dissipation in the regulator, which can otherwise be very high under heavy overload conditions. The drop-out voltage is 2 volts for 5 volt types, and 2.5 volts for other voltages. In other words, for the regulator to work properly the input voltage must always be at least 2 or 2.5 volts higher than the output voltage.

There are a variety of output voltages available, in both positive and negative earth versions, and with several maximum output current levels. These lists should aid the selection of a suitable device for a given application.

100mA Types

Voltage	Positive	Negative
5	µA78L05	µA79L05
8	µA78L08	—
12	µA78L12	µA79L12
15	µA78L15	µA79L15
24	µA78L24	µA79L24

500mA Types

Voltage	Positive	Negative
5	µA78M05	µA79M05
12	µA78M12	µA79M12
15	µA78M15	µA79M15
24	µA78M24	µA79M24

1A Types

Voltage	Positive	Negative
5	μA7805	μA7905
6	μA7806	–
8	μA7808	μA7908
12	μA7812	μA7912
15	μA7815	μA7915
18	μA7818	–
24	μA7824	μA7924

2A Types

Voltage	Positive	Negative
5	μA78S05	–
12	μA78S12	–
15	μA78S15	–
24	μA78S24	

Variable Regulators

Some applications require a supply voltage that is not one of these standard voltages, or must provide a variable output voltage. It is possible to vary the output voltage of a fixed voltage regulator with the aid of some additional components, but this generally gives reduced performance and the degree of variation available is relatively limited. Variable voltage monolithic voltage regulators are available, and these provide excellent performance but are very simple to use. The original devices were four terminal types, but there are now three terminal adjustable devices. We will consider both types here.

Starting with the four terminal types, these are similar to the ordinary fixed voltage types in that they have 'IN', 'OUT', and 'COM' terminals which are used in exactly the same way as for fixed voltage devices. The fourth terminal is a feedback or 'CONT' (control) input, and this connects to the output via a potential divider, as shown in Figure 18. The action of the circuit is to stabilise the 'CONT' input at a nominal figure of 5 volts in standard variable voltage power supply fashion, and with the 'CONT' terminal connected to the output the circuit

functions as a standard 5 volt type. Including the potential divider between the output and the 'CONT' input introduces a voltage drop in the feedback path and boosts the output voltage. Obviously voltages below 5 volts can not be accommodated by this type of regulator circuit.

The output voltage is calculated by first dividing R2 into the sum of R1 and R2 in order to obtain the voltage step-up ratio, and then multiplying this by 5 to give the final answer in volts. For instance, with R2 at 4k7 and R1 at 3k9, this gives a total resistance of 8k6. Dividing this by 4k7 gives a step-up factor of 1.83 (which is a slightly rounded-up figure). Multiplying 5 by 1.83 gives an output voltage of 9.15 volts. For optimum stability the current through the divider circuit should be about 1 milliamp, which means that R2 should always have a value of 4k7 or 5k1. To obtain the required output voltage it is then simply a matter of using a value for R1 that has a value in kilohms which is equal to the figure obtained by deducting 5 from the required output potential. This is only a rather rough-and-ready way of doing things, but the output voltage can not be set precisely using fixed value resistors. Where good accuracy is essential it is a matter of using a fixed resistor and a variable type in series to provide the R1 resistance, and then adjusting the variable resistance in order to obtain precisely the required output voltage.

Four terminal regulators are available as both positive and negative types, but note that with the negative types the 'CONT' terminal is stabilised at 2.23 volts. R2 should therefore be 2k2 in value, and the output voltage is calculated by multiplying 2.23 by the step-up factor of the potential divider circuit. The list provided below gives basic details of some readily available four terminal regulators. Note that the maximum output potential is 30 volts for all types except the μA78HG where the relevant figure is 24 volts. Output noise figures are similar to those of three terminal types, but line and load regulation are only guaranteed to be 1% or less. However, typical figures are somewhat better, especially at low output voltages. With all voltage regulators of this general type the performance reduces somewhat as the output voltage is increased. All these devices incorporate fold-back current limiting incidentally.

Device	Type	Current	Input V. Range
μA78MGU1C	Positive	500mA	7.5 to 40V
μA78GU1C	Positive	1A	7.5 to 40V
μA78HG	Positive	5A	8 to 40V
μA79MGU1C	Negative	500mA	−7 to −30V
μA79GU1C	Negative	1A	−7 to −40V

Three Terminal

Recently the four terminal regulators have been losing ground to three terminal adjustable types. These operate in the configuration shown in the circuit diagram of Figure 19. The action of this

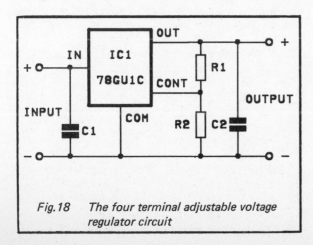

Fig.18   The four terminal adjustable voltage regulator circuit

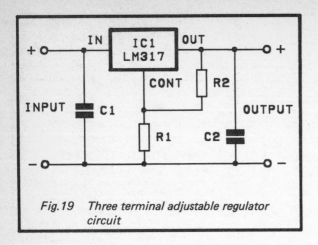

Fig.19 *Three terminal adjustable regulator circuit*

Device	Current	Output V. Range	Drop-out V.
LM317L	100mA	1.25 to 37V	1.8V
LM317M	500mA	1.25 to 37V	1.8V
LM317T	1.5A	1.25 to 37V	2.25V
LM317K	1.5A	1.25 to 37V	2.5V
LM338K	5A	1.25 to 32V	2.9V
LM337L	100mA	−1.25 to −37V	2.75V
LM337T	1.5A	−1.25 to −37V	2.75V

views, even where the devices have standard TO−3 or TO−92 transistor style encapsulations (which are normally shown as base views).

Current Regulators

In some applications it is a stabilised current flow rather than a regulated voltage that is required. There are numerous constant current generator configurations in common use, but for most purposes the very basic type of Figure 21(a) is suitable. R1 and the two diodes provide a base voltage to TR1 which is stabilised at around 1.3 volts below the positive supply potential. This gives about 0.65 volts or so across emitter resistor R2, and with the specified value this sets the emitter current close to 100 microamps. With a high gain device such as the BC559 specified for the TR1 position there is little difference between the collector and emitter currents, and this gives a 1 microamp current flow in the output circuit.

Of course, this only works properly if the load resistance across the output is low enough to enable the set current to flow with the maximum output voltage that the circuit can provide. This voltage is about 1 volt less than the supply voltage. The maximum supply voltage for the circuit is 30 volts, which is imposed by the voltage ratings of the BC559. Using a higher voltage device will enable correspondingly higher voltages to be accommodated. Practically any silicon pnp device is suitable for the TR1 position, but the current gain of the device should be about one hundred or more. The output current is easily changed, and this merely requires the value of R2 to be changed. The required value is obtained by dividing 0.65 by the required current in amps, and this gives an answer in ohms. Alternatively 0.65 can be divided by the required output current given in milliamps, and this gives an answer in kilohms. For example, for a 0.5 milliamp output current a 1k3 component would be needed (0.65 divided by 0.5 = 1.3). The circuit will work with currents from around 1 microamp to about 50 milliamps, but at high currents make sure that the dissipation in TR1 is kept within the operating limits of the particular device used.

The circuit of Figure 21(b) is the current sink equivalent of the current source circuit of Figure 21(a), and it operates in precisely the same way.

In Figure 21(c) a constant current generator integrated circuit is used, and the LM334Z has an

circuit is to stabilise the output voltage 1.25 volts above the potential at the 'CONT' input. The potential divider formed by R1 and R2 is used to raise the 'CONT' terminal above earth potential, and thus boost the output voltage. The supply current for the regulator flows through R1, but this is only about 5 microamps. Therefore, provided the current through R1 is kept much higher than this figure, variations in the supply current drawn by the device will not significantly affect the output voltage. With R2 set at 240 ohms in value, the current through the divider is one hundred times the supply current, which should give good results in practice. The value for R1 is given by taking the required output voltage minus 1.25, and then multiplying this by 240. This gives an answer in ohms. For example, for an output voltage of 5.75 volts, first deduct 1.25 from this to give the voltage across R1, which is obviously 4.5 volts, and then multiply this by 240 to give a value for R1 of 1080 ohms (1.08k). Obviously 1k is the nearest preferred value, but as for the four terminal devices, a fixed resistor and a variable type in series must be used if the output voltage must be set with a high degree of precision.

The performance of these three terminal adjustable devices is extremely good, with line and load regulation at typical figures of around 0.01 and 0.1% respectively, which is considerably more than adequate for most applications. The output noise figure is not quite so impressive at 150 microvolts, although this is still more than adequate for most requirements. The input voltage range is 3V (approximately) to 40 volts. There are now a few negative types available, and these offer similar performance levels to the positive types. The table oppositve gives brief details of the readily available types. It includes the drop-out voltage which varies significantly from one type to another.

Figure 20 gives pinout details for a wide range of voltage regulators. A point to watch when dealing with these devices is that the positive and negative types have different pinout arrangements. Also note that in Figure 20 the pinout diagrams are all top

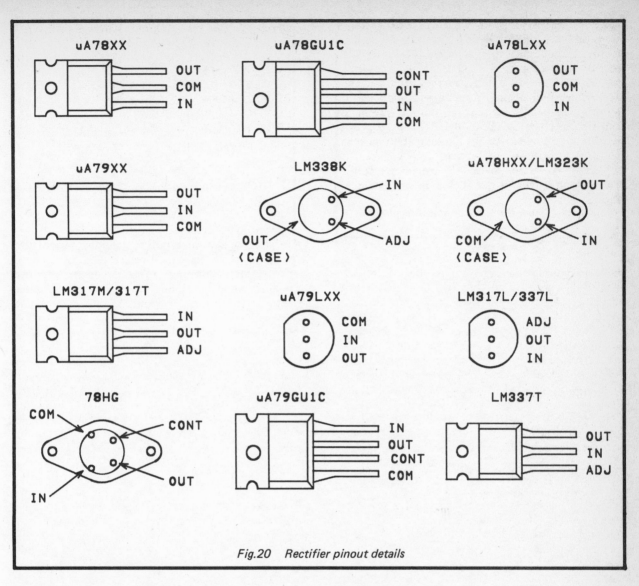

Fig.20   Rectifier pinout details

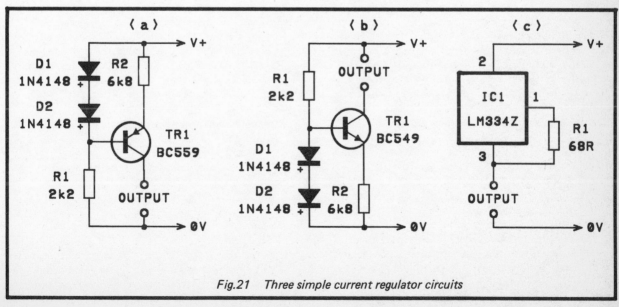

Fig.21   Three simple current regulator circuits

29

operating current range of 1 microamp to 10 milliamps and will operate over a 1 to 40 volt supply range. Current regulation is 0.02% per volt. The resistor sets the output current, which is about 1 milliamp with the value shown on the circuit diagram. The value required for a given current is calculated by dividing 0.0677 by required output current in amps. Note that with all these circuits a preset resistor should be used if the output current must be set very accurately, and that the output current is subject to a certain amount of temperature drift. The pinout details of the LM334Z are shown in Figure 22.

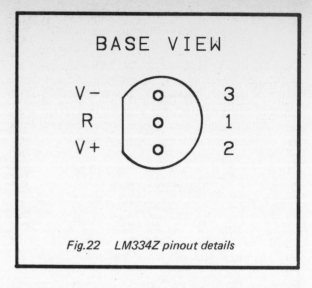

BASE VIEW

V−   o   3
R   o   1
V+   o   2

Fig.22   LM334Z pinout details

CIRCUIT SYMBOLS

Figures 23 to 25 show a range of circuit symbols. I would not claim that every circuit symbol is included in these diagrams, but the vast majority of circuit symbols that you will ever encounter are included here. When dealing with circuit diagrams it is essential to bear in mind that there are bound to be variations in the exact appearance of symbols due to differences of style. In particular, some transistor symbols are much more basic than others. Also, in some cases there are two totally different symbols for the same component, and the box and zig-zag resistor symbols are a good example of this. The British standard resistor symbol is the box type, but for historical reasons most electronic hobbyist magazines use the zig-zag type, as do some equipment manufacturers and others. Another common example of what might be called a 'double standard' is the cross-over, where two wires cross without connecting to one another. The most popular form of cross-over is the type where the two lines are both straight, but there is a different style where one wire loops over the other. Where applicable the circuit symbol diagrams often show both versions of a symbol.

There is a style of circuit where virtually all two terminal components are shown as box-resistor type symbols. These can be a bit confusing and difficult to read, but fortunately this system seems to be a rarity and is something you are not likely to encounter. The only way of telling what type of component each box-type symbol represents is to look at the component identification and value labels.

Logic symbols have in the past been the cause of a great deal of confusion with several different sets of symbols in common use. These days things seem to have settled down with those shown in Figure 25 being the ones almost universally used these days. Note that although the Schmitt Trigger symbol in Figure 25 is a 2 input NAND gate, the additional marking can be added to any gate, inverter, or buffer to indicate that it has built-in triggering. This marking, incidentally, is derived from the input/output voltage transfer characteristic of a Schmitt Trigger.

The operational amplifier circuit symbol is the only special one used for linear integrated circuits. All other types simply use a box symbol, apart from amplifiers which often 'borrow' the operational amplifier triangular shape, suitably elongated where necessary, to accommodate extra terminals. Note that the '+' and '−' signs (which respectively indicate the non-inverting and inverting inputs) are often omitted from the operational amplifier circuit symbol.

As with the symbols themselves, there is some divergence when it comes to the identification letters used for component numbers, and while transistors are 'TRn' on most circuits, both 'Trn' and 'Qn' are quite often encountered as well. This list of component identification letters should be useful for reference purposes.

Letter(s)	Component
B	Battery
BY	Battery
C	Capacitor (any fixed value type)
CH	Chassis
CRT	Cathode ray tube
CSR	Thyristor or triac (controlled silicon rectifier)
D	Diode (any type including photo-diodes, rectifiers, and light emitting types)
E	Earth
FL	Filter (usually ceramic, mechanical, or crystal type)
FS	Fuse
JK	Jack socket
IC	Integrated Circuit
IFT	Intermediate frequency transformer
L	Inductor (fixed or variable)
LP	Lamp (neon or filament, but not LED)
LS	Loudspeaker
M	Motor
ME	Meter
Mic	Microphone
PCC	Photo conductive cell (photo-resistor, usually a cadmium sulphide type)
PL	Plug (any type)
Q	Transistor
R	Resistor (fixed value)
RLA	Relay (coil or contacts)
S	Switch
SK	Socket (any type, but jack types often given 'JK' identification letters)
SW	Switch
T	Transformer (any type including RF)
TC	Trimmer capacitor (i.e. preset variable capacitor)
Th	Thermistor
TL	Earphone or headphones
Tr	Transistor
TR	Transistor
V	Valve (any type except CRT)
VC	Variable capacitor
VR	Variable resistor or potentiometer
WD	Warning device (horn or bell)
X	Crystal

On bipolar transistor circuit symbols (and leadout diagrams) the letters 'e', 'b', and 'c' are sometimes used to respectively indicate the emitter, base, and collector terminals. For field effect devices the corresponding letters are 's', 'g', and 'd', indicating the source, gate, and drain terminals respectively.

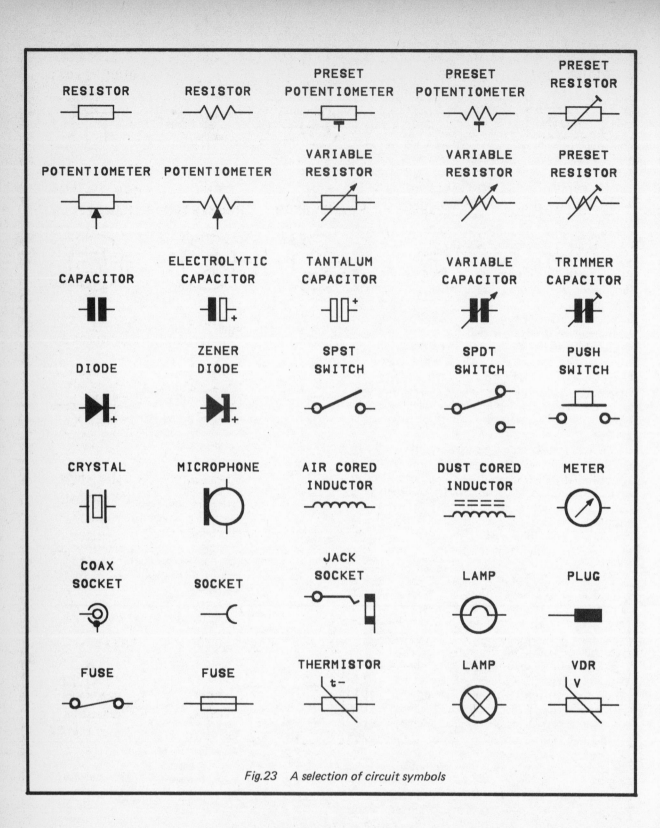

Fig.23   A selection of circuit symbols

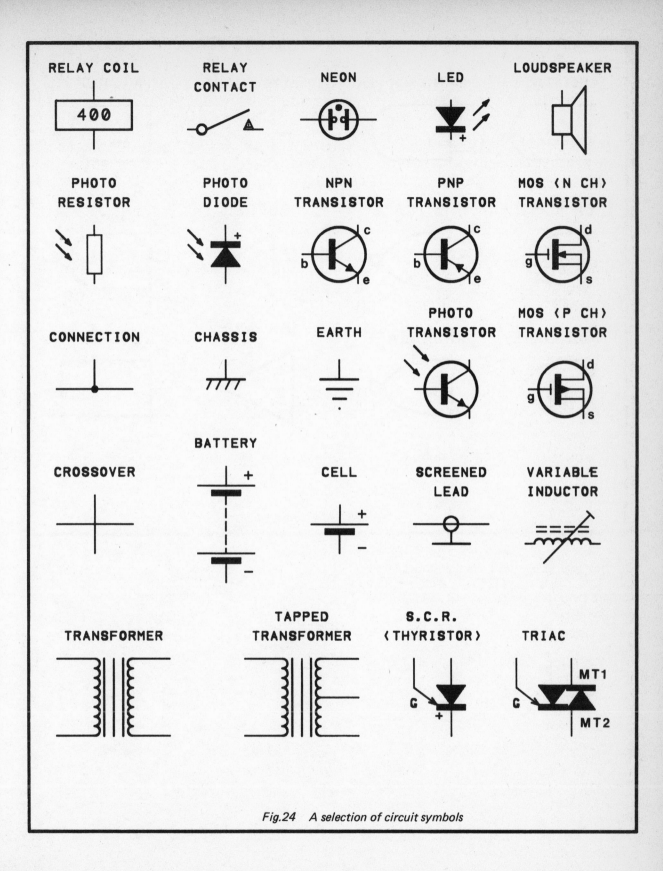

Fig.24   A selection of circuit symbols

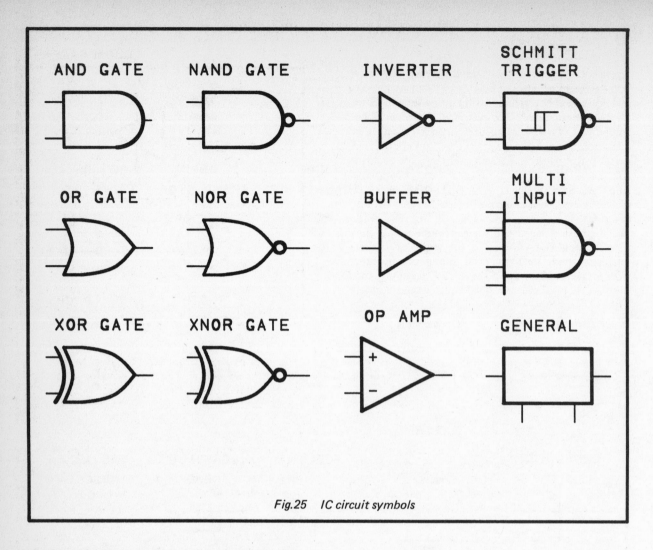

AND GATE   NAND GATE   INVERTER   SCHMITT TRIGGER

OR GATE   NOR GATE   BUFFER   MULTI INPUT

XOR GATE   XNOR GATE   OP AMP   GENERAL

Fig.25   IC circuit symbols

'G' for gate is also used on thyristors and triacs, and with the latter 'MT1' and 'MT2' are used to denote the mains terminal 1 and mains terminal 2 connections.

OPERATIONAL AMPLIFIERS

Operational amplifiers are undoubtedly the most popular form of linear integrated circuit at present, and seem likely to remain so for some time to come. They were originally designed for use in analogue computers where they performed mathematical operations, and it is from this that the 'operational' part of the name is derived. These days analogue computers are virtually extinct, but operational amplifiers live on in a wide range of applications including test gear, audio equipment, motor control, and robotics.

An unusual aspect of these components is their power supply requirements — they are designed for operation with dual balanced supplies. In other words, rather than (say) a single 12 volt supply, twin supplies of plus and minus 12 volts would be used, with a central 0 volt supply rail. The reason for this arrangement being used originally was that the output voltage of the amplifier represented the answer to a calculation, and the ability to produce voltages of both polarities meant that both positive and negative numbers could be represented. It is still quite common for circuits using these devices to have dual supply rails, but probably the majority have only a single supply. This is perfectly satisfactory in audio amplification and similar applications where the input of the amplifier can be biased in order to permit A.C. coupled input signals to be handled properly. It is also permissible in D.C. applications where negative output voltages will never be required, but only if the operational amplifiers used are types designed for single supply operation. The CA3130E and CA3140 are probably the best known devices of this type.

Modes

For general amplification purposes operational amplifiers are an attractive choice as they enable the voltage gain and input impedance of the circuit to be set very accurately and using only very basic mathematics to find the correct circuit values. Figure 26 shows the basic inverting amplifier mode of operation, and this requires only two resistors to set the voltage gain and input impedance. As its name suggests, the signal is subjected to a 180 degree phase shift between the input and output of the circuit. This will often be of no consequence, but is something that should be borne in mind when using this configuration.

The input impedance is simply equal to the value given to R1. The voltage gain is equal to R2/R1. Thus, in order to obtain a certain combination of input impedance and voltage gain it is merely necessary to give R1 a value which is equal to the required input impedance, and then multiply this value by the required voltage gain in order to obtain the correct value for R2.

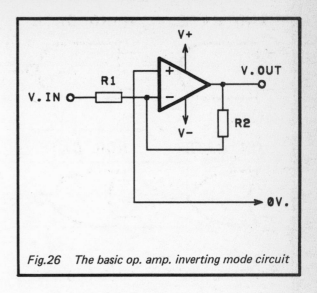

Fig.26   The basic op. amp. inverting mode circuit

This is perhaps deceptively simple in that what is fine in theory does not necessarily work in practice. In theory the operational amplifier has an infinite innate voltage gain (termed the 'open-loop voltage gain'), and an infinite bandwidth. It also has no input capacitance in theory. In practice the voltage gain of the amplifier is generally very high at D.C. (about 200000 times), but this reduces at 6dB per octave above frequencies of only around 10 Hertz. The graph of Figure 27 shows the open loop frequency response of the industry standard μA741C operational amplifier. The voltage gain set by the feedback resistors (which is called the 'closed loop voltage gain') can only be maintained up to frequencies where the open loop voltage gain is higher than the required closed loop gain. An important operational amplifier parameter is the unity gain bandwidth (i.e. the frequency at which the open loop voltage gain falls to unity). For the standard μA741C this is 1MHz, as can be seen from Figure 27. With the usual 6dB per octave roll-off this makes it easy to calculate the closed loop voltage gain for various bandwidths. It is simply a matter of dividing the unity gain bandwidth by the voltage gain (e.g. with a gain of 5 times this gives 1000000 Hertz divided by 5, which gives a bandwidth of 200000 Hertz, or 200kHz in other words).

It is apparent from this that operational amplifiers are not suitable for applications where a mixture of high gain and wide bandwidth are required, apart from a few special (and quite expensive) types. Some devices offer a higher unity gain bandwidth than the μA741C, but the actual figure is still generally only about 3 or 4MHz. This only represents a bandwdth of 3 or 4kHz with a voltage gain of 1000 times. For high gain even at audio frequencies it is generally necessary to use two or three amplifiers in series, and

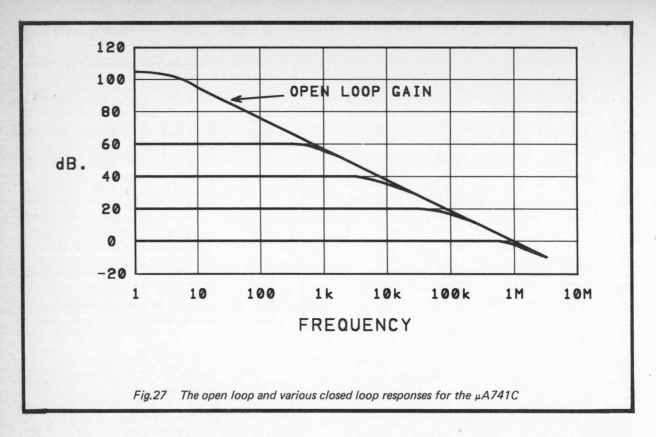

Fig.27   *The open loop and various closed loop responses for the µA741C*

few operational amplifiers offer worthwhile performance much above the upper limit of the audio band.

A combination of high input impedance and even moderate voltage gain is something that is beyond the capability of the inverting mode circuit. One problem is that of R2 requiring an impractically large value. The other main problem is that of stray capacitance in the circuit, especially the input capacitance of the operational amplifier. This can tend to produce strong irregularities in the frequency response, especially with some of the modern FET input devices which have relatively high input capacitance figures. Where high gain and input impedance are required it is necessary to use a unity or low voltage gain input stage followed by one or two voltage amplifiers.

The µA741C operational amplifier is a type which has internal frequency compensation. This simply means that it has an internal capacitor which provides the 6dB per octave roll-off. The purpose of this built-in filtering is to prevent instability, and with internally compensated devices stability is normally guaranteed at any voltage gain right down to unity (assuming that the component layout is such that it does not introduce instability, of course). With externally compensated devices the roll-off rate is controlled by the discrete compensation circuit (which is often just a single capacitor), and it can be tailored to suit the closed loop gain of the circuit. For unity gain amplifiers there is no advantage in using external compensation, as the

bandwidth would have to be limited to the same figure as for an equivalent internally compensated circuit. For higher gains though, a higher unity gain bandwidth can be used, thus allowing a wider bandwidth for a given voltage gain. The µA748C is the externally compensated equivalent to the µA741C type, and with a 2pF compensation capacitance and a voltage gain of one hundred times this gives a bandwidth of around 100kHz, which is about ten times that obtained from a µA741C with the same gain and its internal 30pF compensation capacitor.

Returning to amplifier modes, the other type is the non-inverting variety, and this uses the configuration shown in Figure 28. Here R3 sets the input impedance, and this is again equal to the value of the component used here. This is actually a rather over-simplified way of looking at things, and it is the input resistance that is equal to the value of R3. At high frequencies the input capacitance of the operational amplifier will usually result in some reduction of the input impedance, and if R3 has a high value of a few hundred kilohms or more there may well be a massive reduction in the input impedance at high frequencies. In fact the input resistance of the operational amplifier could significantly shunt R3 if a high value is used here, but where high input resistance is required it is normal to use a Jfet or MOSFET input device. These have an input resistance of around one million megohms, which is high enough to ensure that there is no significant shunting of R3 even if it has a value of many megohms.

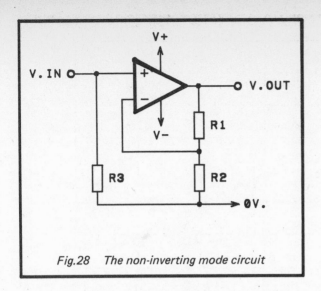

Fig.28   The non-inverting mode circuit

impedance of several megohms together with a voltage gain of ten or even a hundred times, but such a combination might be unusable in practice. This is just a matter of stray feedback causing instability, and the fact that the input and output of the circuit are in-phase helps to encourage this instability. In practice it might still be preferable to use to separate stages to give the required combination of gain and input impedance, as good isolation between the input and the output of the circuit are then much more easily obtained.

The circuits of Figures 26 and 28 are for the standard D.C. coupled circuits. For audio amplification it is more normal for the circuits of Figure 29 (inverting) and Figure 30 (non-inverting) to be used.

R1 and R2 control the voltage gain of the circuit, but not in quite the same way as for the inverting mode circuit. The voltage gain is equal to $(R1 + R2)/R2$. Or another way of looking at things is to divide R1 into R2, and then add 1 to this to give the final figure. For instance, with R1 at 10k and R2 at 1k, dividing the former by the latter gives a figure of 10, and then adding 1 to this gives the final voltage gain figure of 11.

To choose suitable values for a given voltage gain, first select a reasonable value for R1 (somewhere around 10k is usually satisfactory), and then divide this by one less than the required voltage gain to obtain the correct value for R2. For example, for a voltage gain of six times and with R1 set at 10k, dividing 10k by one less than the required voltage gain gives 10k/5, which obviously gives an answer of 2k. The exact resistance through R1 and R2 is not critical, but if it is very low it loads the output of the operational amplifier very heavily and could seriously impair the performance of the circuit. On the other hand, a very high resistance here could interact with the input capacitance of the amplifier and other stray circuit capacitances to give pronounced irregularities in the frequency response. A total resistance of around 10 to 20k is comfortably between these two extremes and will normally give good results.

Note that for unity voltage gain R1 and R2 are unnecessary — the inverting input should be connected direct to the output. There is no significant difference between the bandwidth of an inverting mode circuit and a non-inverting equivalent, with the unity gain bandwidth placing the same constraints on performance in both cases. Although the non-inverting mode may seem to offer better prospects where a combination of moderate voltage gain and high input impedance are required, this is not necessarily the case. There is certainly no difficulty in implementing suitable values to give an input

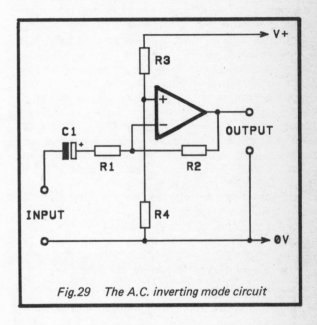

Fig.29   The A.C. inverting mode circuit

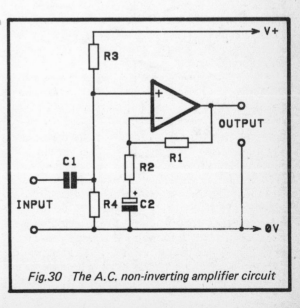

Fig.30   The A.C. non-inverting amplifier circuit

These are essentially the same as the D.C. circuits, but have bias resistors and D.C. blocking capacitors added. In the case of the non-inverting circuit, the input impedance is equal to half the value given to R3 and R4 (and these would normally be of equal value).

Operational amplifiers have good immunity to noise on the supply rails, offering what is normally about 70 to 100dB of rejection. With the A.C. amplifier circuits this immunity will be largely lost unless supply decoupling networks are included in the bias networks.

Offset Null

In theory the output voltage from an operational amplifier circuit should be 0 volts with no input applied, but in practice the output voltage usually drifts slightly from the correct level due to input offsets. These offset voltages are normally very low at a few millivolts or so, but they are amplified by an amount equal to the closed loop voltage gain of the circuit, and quite large errors in the output voltage can occur. For critical applications there are special 'instrumentation' devices which are guaranteed to have extremely low offset levels. These are mostly quite expensive devices though, which cost many times more than the μA741C and similar devices. An alternative approach is to use and offset null to trim the output voltage to the correct quiescent level. This is not as good as having a high quality component with minimal offset voltages, mainly due to the temperature drift which can necessitate quite frequency retrimming of the offset null control in critical applications. It is a very low cost solution to the problem through.

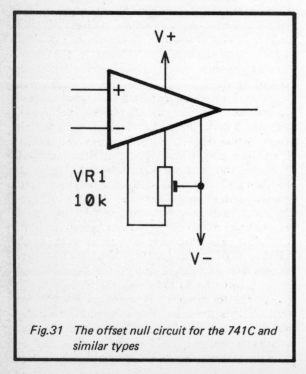

Fig.31   The offset null circuit for the 741C and
similar types

Figure 31 shows the offset null control circuit for the μA741C operational amplifier, and many other types also use the same offset null circuit (the LF351 and NE531 for example). Not all types use this method though, and Figure 32 shows the offset null controls for three devices that do not. Actually, the LM311 is not an operational amplifier, but is a voltage comparator. Operational amplifiers are often used as voltage comparators, and in this mode the two voltages to be compared are simply fed one to each input. Operation in this mode relies upon the fact that operational amplifiers are differential amplifiers. In other words, it is the difference across the two inputs that is amplified, and the absolute voltage levels are not relevant. Also, due to the very high gain of these devices, very little voltage difference is required across the inputs in order to send the output fully negative or positive. Therefore, if the non-inverting input is slightly higher in voltage than the inverting input the output goes high, or if it is lower in voltage the output goes fully negative.

Voltage comparators are much the same as operational amplifiers, and most types can actually be used as amplifiers. However, their characteristics are optimised for performance in comparator applications, and they are often capable of operation from single supply rails (or sometimes non-balanced dual supplies such as +10 and −5 volts) with their inputs at virtually any potentials within or just outside the supply voltages. They are also generally capable of high speed switching, and in many cases seem to have open collector output stages.

Other Parameters

There are numerous parameters in operational amplifier data sheets, and we will briefly deal with some of the more important ones here.

Slew Rate

The slew rate is the maximum rate at which the output of the amplifier can change, and is normally specified in volts per microsecond. The main point here is that the fact that an amplifier can provide (say) a bandwidth of 100kHz does not mean that it can provide this bandwidth at all signal levels. Large signals may require the output to change at a faster rate than it is actually capable of achieving, and this causes the signal to be distorted and reduced in amplitude. This is called slewing induced distortion (or just 'SID'). It is only an important factor where the amplifier must handle high level high frequency signals.

Large Signal Bandwidth

This is just another way of measuring slew rate, and it is the highest frequency at which the amplifier can provide its full output voltage swing.

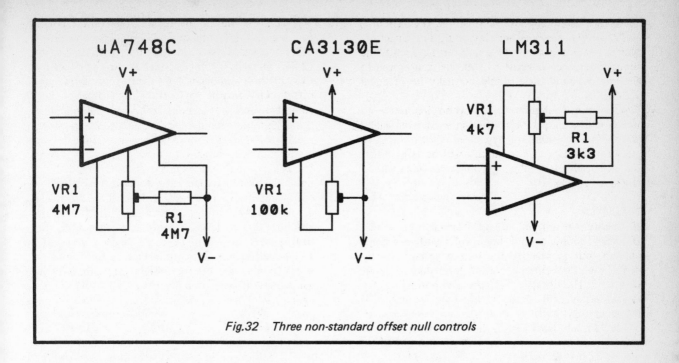

Fig.32   Three non-standard offset null controls

Common Mode Rejection

In theory a signal applied to both inputs will not produce any change in the output voltage as it will not alter the differential input voltage. In practice there will be some change in the output voltage, and this is a measure of how much signal breaks through to the output.

Latch-Up

Ideally an operational amplifier should operate properly with its inputs at any voltages within the supply limits. With some types this is not the case though, and in extreme cases taking the input voltages outside certain limits results in the device latching-up, which means that the output goes to a voltage that is inappropriate for the comparative input voltages. As the name implies, the device may even latch in this state, and not operate properly once permissible input levels have been restored. This is not to say that the device will have been damaged — it may well function properly again if the supply is cut off momentarily.

Output Voltage Swing

This is merely the maximum positive and negative output voltages for a given supply voltage. Ideally it would be equal to the supply voltage and some modern devices approach this level of performance, but many types can not provide output levels within about two or three volts of each supply rail.

Output Resistance

An ideal operational amplifier has zero output resistance, so that loading of the output does not cause any reduction in the output voltage. Practical devices have quite low output resistances of about 75 ohms, and the application of negative feedback can reduce this to under 1 ohm. This does not mean that an operational amplifier can be used as a power amplifier, it merely means that medium to high impedances can be driven without any significant loading effects. Apart from a few high current devices, operational amplifiers incorporate output short circuit protection circuits which give a short circuit output current of typically about 10 to 20 milliamps. Trying to drive a low impedance load with a high signal level will merely result in the current limiting coming into operation and clipping the output signal.

Table 2 provides basic data on a wide range of operational amplifiers and should be useful when selecting a device for a given application. Figure 33 shows pinout details for a wide range of 8 pin DIL operational amplifiers. Note that there are many types not shown in this diagram but which have the standard µA741C pinout configuration. This includes popular devices such as the bifet TL071 and TL081 devices. Similarly, there are numerous dual devices which have the same pinout configuration as the LM1458C, and this includes devices such as the LF353, TL072, and LM358. Most of these dual devices are electrically identical to popular single devices, with the LF353 being the dual version of the LF351 for instance. However, with these 8 pin dual versions there are no pins available for offset null terminals, and this facility is therefore not avaialble with these.

Many of these devices are produced by more than

TABLE 2

Device	B.Width	Supply	S.Rate	Input R	Type/Comp
CA3130E	15MHz	5–16V/2mA	10V/μs	1.5T	MOS/EXT
CA3140E	4.5MHz	4–36V/4mA	9V/μs	1.5T	MOS/INT
CA3240E		Dual version of CA3140E			
LF351	4MHz	±5–36V/1m4	13V/μs	1T	BIF/INT
LF353		Dual version of LF351			
LF347		Quad version of LF351			
LF411	4MHz	±5–18V/5m6	15V/μs	1T	BIF/INT
LF412		Dual version of LF411			
LF441	1MHz	±5–18V/150μA	1V/μs	1T	BIF/INT
LF442		Dual version of LF441			
LF444		Quad version of LF441			
LM301	1MHz	±5–18V/1m8	0.4V/μs	2M	BIP/EXT
LM308	1MHz	±5–18V/0m3	0.2V/μs	40M	BIP/EXT
LM324	1MHz	3–32V/1m5	0.5V/μs	1M	BIP/INT
LM1458C	1MHz	±3–18V/3mA	0.5V/μs	1M	BIP/INT
NE531	1MHz	±5–22V/10mA	35V/μs	20M	BIP/EXT
NE5534	10MHz	±3–20V/4mA	13V/μs	100k	BIP/EXT
NE5532		Dual version of NE5534			
OP-07C	0.5MHz	±2.5–22V/2m7	0.17V/μs	33M	BIP/INT
OP-27G	8MHz	±5–22V/3m5	2.8V/μs	4M	BIP/INT
RC4136	3MHz	±3–18V/7mA	1V/μs	5M	BIP/INT
TL061	1MHz	±2–18V/200μA	3.5V/μs	1T	BIF/INT
TL062		Dual version of TL061			
TL064		Quad version of TL061			
TL071	3MHz	±2–18V/1mA	13V/μs	1T	BIF/INT
TL072		Dual version of TL071			
TL074		Quad version of TL071			
TL081	3MHz	±2–18V/1m4	13V/μs	1T	BIF/INT
TL082		Dual version of TL081			
TL084		Quad version of TL081			
μA741C	1MHz	±5–18V/1m7	0.5V/μs	2M	BIP/INT
μA747		Dual version of μA741C			
μA748C	1MHz	±5–18V/1m7	0.5V/μs	2M	BIP/EXT

$$(T = 10^{12})$$

Note that where the supply range is not given in plus/minus form the device is suitable for single supply operation. Dual balanced supplies are also perfectly usable with these devices, but the total series voltage of the two supplies must not exceed the maximum figure (e.g. with a 32 volt maximum rating for single supply operation the maximum permissible dual supply voltage is plus and minus 16 volts). At the other end of the supply range the total voltage of the two supplies must be at least equal to the quoted minimum supply figure (e.g. a 4 volt minimum supply voltage rating is equivalent to a dual supply of plus and minus 2 volts). With externally compensated devices the bandwidth and slew rate figures depend on the values used in the external frequency compensation circuit, and the above figures are no more than a rough guide (in most cases gives the bandwidth and slew rate for a device which is compensated for unity voltage gain). In the 'TYPE/COMP' column these abbreviations are used:

BIF	Bifet device
BIP	Bipolar device
MOS	MOSFET input stage device
EXT	External frequency compensation
INT	Internal frequency compensation

The following list are for categories of operational amplifier, and these should help to quickly located a suitable device for a given application.

General Purpose

Single
μA741C (Industry standard internally compensated)
μA748C (externally compensated μA741C)
LM301 ('improved' 748C)
LM308 (low current LM301)
Dual
LM1458C (effectively dual 741C with no offset null)
Quad
3403 (quad version of LM1458C)

High Quality Audio

Single
LF351 (low distortion Bifet type)
NE5534 (ultra-low noise and distortion bipolar type)
TL061 (low current Bifet type)
TL071 (low noise Bifet type)
TL081 (standard Bifet type)
ZN424P (ultra-low noise and distortion bipolar type)
Dual
LF353 (dual LF351)
NE5532 (dual NE5534)
TL062 (dual TL061)
TL072 (dual TL071)
TL082 (dual TL081)

Quad
LF447 (quad LF351)
TL064 (quad TL061)
TL074 (quad TL071)
TL084 (quad TL081)

Single Supply Operation

Single
CA3130E (MOS input stage and CMOS output stage)
CA3140E (MOS input stage and class A output stage)
Dual
CA3240E (dual CA3140E)
CA3240E-1 (dual CA3140E including offset null)
LM358 (bipolar type)
Quad
LM324 (quad bipolar low current type)

Instrumentation

Single
LF356 (bifet type)
LM725C (bipolar type)

OP-07C (bipolar type)
OP-27G (bipolar low noise type)
OP-37C (bipolar low noise high speed type)

Very Low Power Consumption

Single
ICL7611 (programmable power consumption)
LF441 (bifet type)
TL061 (bifet type)
Dual
ICL7621 (dual ICL7611)
ICL7622 (dual ICL7611 with offset null)
LF442 (dual LF441)
TL062 (dual TL061)
Quad
LF444 (quad LF441)
TL064 (quad TL061)

one manufacturer, and the type numbers sometimes vary slightly from one manufacturer to another. This is usually in the form of different prefixes. For example, the LM1458C from National Semiconductors is also available as the CA1458C from R.C.A. Some component suppliers do not use a particular manufacturers type number for some of these devices, but instead just list them under the basic type number (1458C, 741C, 748C, etc.).

Another point to bear in mind is that some devices are available in more than one encapsulation. The 741C is normally sold in its 8 pin DIL form, but there are 14 pin DIL and 8 pin TO-99 metal encapsulated types as well, and the same is also true of the 748C and some other types. Figure 34 gives pinout details for the three versions of the 741C. All the other types I have encountered which are available in more than one type of encapsulation have always conformed to this general scheme of things. Sometimes a suffix is used to denote the package type. For example, with the CA3130 an 'E' suffix shows that the device is the normal 8 pin DIL plastic type, and 'T' indicates that it has a TO-99 metal encapsulation, and an 'S' suffix shows that it has a TO-99 encapsulation with the leadout wires preformed into the 8 pin DIL configuration.

Figure 35 gives pinout details for some 14 pin multiple operational amplifier devices. The μA747C is a dual μA741C, but unlike the 8 pin dual types it does include offset null terminals, and even separate positive supply inputs for the two amplifiers. The LM324 is a popular quad device, and with this device no offset null terminals are provided. Many quad devices, including the TL064/74/84 range, use the same basic configuration. One quad device that does not is the RC4136, as can be seen from Figure 35. The CA3240E-1 should not be confused with the CA3240E. The latter is 8 pin dual version of the CA3140E, whereas the device with the '-1' suffix is a 14 pin type which includes the offset null terminals for both amplifiers.

Finally, Figure 36 gives pinout details for what might be termed pseudo operational amplifiers. The LM710, MC3302, LM311, and LM319 are voltage comparators rather than true operational amplifiers. The LM3900 is a quad 'Norton' or current differencing amplifier. The output voltage of a Norton amplifier is governed by the differential input current rather than by the input voltage difference, and it must be used in suitably modified circuit configurations. These are less used now than they once were, and this is probably due to the fact they were intended for operational amplifier style circuits but with a single supply rail. Operational amplifiers such as the CA3140E, LM358, and LM324 now offer what is in most cases superior performance in single supply applications.

The CA3080E and LM13600N are operational transconductance amplifiers. These are another form of current differencing amplifier, but their most important characteristic is the ability to control their gain via a bias current fed to the amplifier bias input. They are much used in voltage controlled amplifiers, voltage controlled filters, and similar applications.

The ICL7611 is a programmable operational amplifier. By altering the current consumption of the device it is possible to obtain various combinations of bandwidth and power drain. This enables the device to be operated at a very low supply current in applications where low power consumption are of more importance than the bandwidth of the amplifier.

The NE5539 is a wide bandwidth and high slew rate device. Its gain bandwidth product is 1.2GHz, and the slew rate is 600V per microsecond (which compares with 0.5V per microsecond for the standard μA741C). Very careful design is needed in order to obtain good stability with this device though.

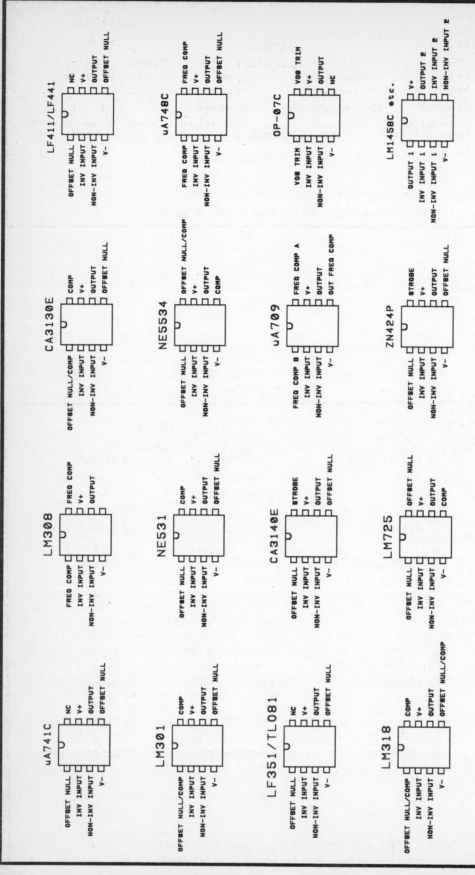

Fig.33   Pinout details for a range of 8 pin DIL operational amplifiers

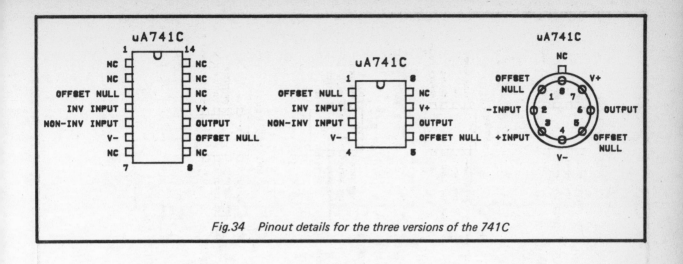

Fig.34   Pinout details for the three versions of the 741C

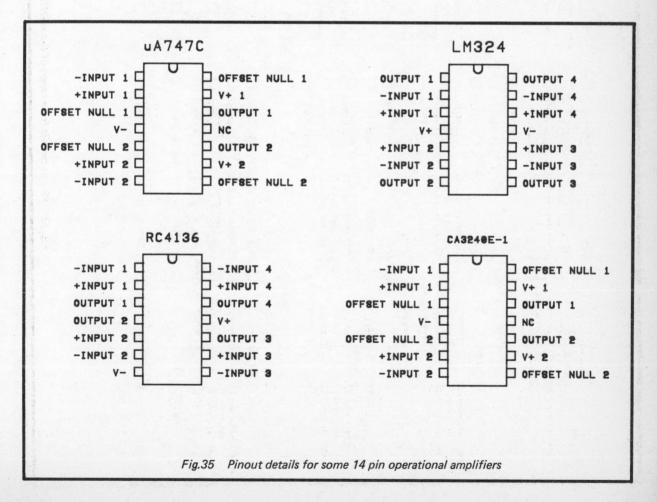

Fig.35   Pinout details for some 14 pin operational amplifiers

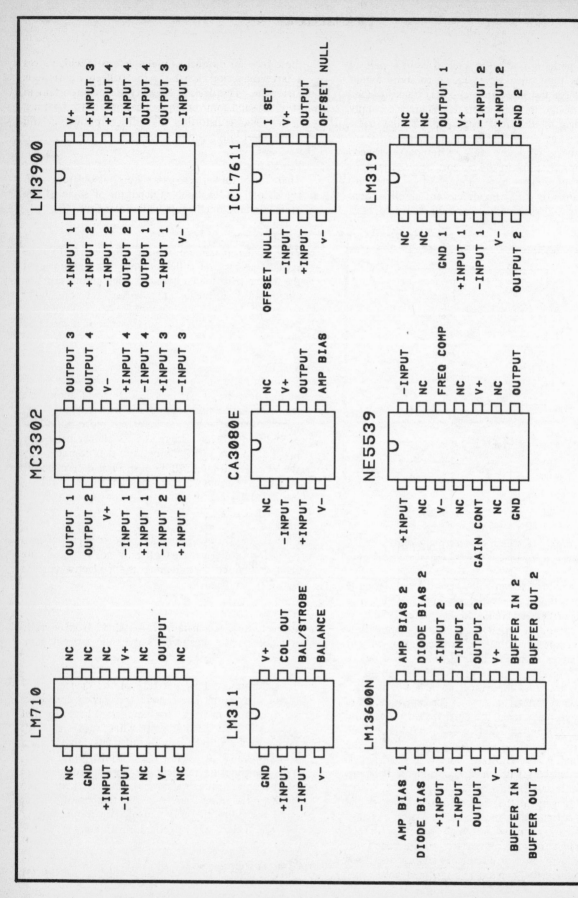

Fig.36   Pinout details for some 'pseud' operational amplifiers

Although perhaps not quite such a central part of projects as they once were, having to some extent been displaced by integrated circuits, transistors are still to be found in many projects. There is certainly no shortage of different types, albeit that some popular devices are available under several different type numbers, with the only differences between them being variations in the encapsulation or leadout configuration. The basic action of an ordinary bipolar transistor is to provide current amplification, and Figure 37 shows the standard transistor test set up.

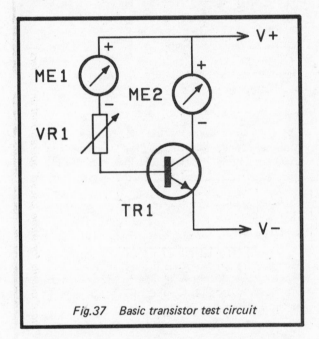

Fig.37   Basic transistor test circuit

VR1 provides a variable base current to the device, and this is measured by meter ME1. The collector current is monitored by meter ME2. As the base current is varied the collector current flow alters in sympathy with it, but the collector current is much larger than the base current. The device therefore provides current gain, and this could be as little as ten times for a low gain device to as much as a thousand times for a very high gain type. It is important to realise that the current gain varies quite considerably from one device of a particular type number to another of the same type. Also, the current gain is not constant for any device, and it varies substantially with changes in collector current, and to a lesser extent with changes in collector voltage. In general the current gain reduces as the collector current is reduced, but the gain can also tend to fall away somewhat at high collector currents. A few radio frequency devices are designed for automatic gain control circuits which use increased bias to reduce the gain on strong signal levels, and

these have an unusual gain characteristic which gives a large reduction in gain as the collector current is increased. This lack of linearity is not important in switching and some other applications, but it obviously introduces distortion in audio amplification and other linear applications.

Parameters

There are numerous parameters associated with transistors, and a brief explanation of some of the more common ones would be in order here.

VCBO

This is the maximum voltage that can safely be applied across the collector and base terminals of the device with the emitter left open circuit (i.e. not connected). Exceeding this voltage rating is likely to result in the component breaking down and probably damaged to the point where it is rendered unusable.

VCEO

Similar to the above parameter, but it is the maximum safe voltage that can be connected across the collector and emitter terminals with the base left open circuit. This is generally the more important of the two voltage ratings as it is almost invariably lower than the VCBO rating, and it is consequently the VCEO figure that will in most cases determine the maximum supply voltage that can be used with a particular device.

hFE

This is the D.C. current gain, and is specified at a particular collector current and voltage (i.e. the figure obtained by dividing the collector current by the base current).

hfe

Whereas hFE is a parameter obtained from a static test, hfe is the small signal dynamic current gain.

Tj

Tj is the junction temperature of the device, and it is the maximum figure that the device can withstand without damage. It is important to realise that practically any component when used at high temperatures will be significantly less reliable than when operated at around room temperature. Also, Tj is the junction temperature (i.e. the temperature of the chip inside the device), and is likely to be significantly more than the case temperature. For good reliability the case temperature should always be well below the specified maximum Tj figure.

IC

There is a limit to the current flow which a transistor

can withstand, and this is the maximum permissible current flow in its collector circuit. The input and output currents both flow in the collector circuit, and so this is generally the most critical current to consider when dealing with these devices. The figures for some medium power types may seem rather high, and this is generally where a pulsed rather than continuous figure is quoted.

PTOT

This is the maximum power rating of the component. In other words, if the collector to emitter voltage is multiplied by the collector current, the power figure this gives must never exceed the PTOT rating of the device. When dealing with power devices it should be borne in mind that the PTOT rating is one that assumes that the device is fitted onto a very large heatsink, and that it is in very good thermal contact with it. The maximum power rating with inefficient or no heat-sinking is likely to be very much less (perhaps less than 10% of the PTOT rating). The PTOT ratings for a few medium power types also assume that the device is provided with a reasonable amount of heat-sinking. Another point to keep in mind when dealing with power ratings is the so-called 'safe area of operation'. This is the range of permitted collector voltage and current combinations for a device. Not all collector voltage and current combinations that keep within the PTOT rating will necessarily be within the safe area of operation.

VEBO

When forward biased the base-emitter junction is very much like a forward biased diode, and for a silicon device this means that the voltage here will never exceed more than about 0.7 volts. The VEBO rating is the maximum reverse bias voltage across the base and emitter terminals. This figure is normally quite low at only around 5 to 8 volts, but this does not mean that a voltage as low as this will necessarily damage a device. When reverse biased the base-emitter junction operates very much like a zener diode, and it 'avalanches' so that the input voltage is clipped at a level which never significantly exceeds the initial 'avalanche' potential. Of course, the current flow must be within the limits of the device, but there is not normally any problem here. However, this voltage rating should be kept in mind when dealing with circuits that use capacitive coupling into the base of a transistor, as this voltage rating can then be exceeded. Although the transistor is unlikely to be damaged, this 'avalanche' effect can upset the operation of the circuit. In particular, it can prevent some types of oscillator from working properly unless the supply voltage is suitably restricted, or other precautions are taken.

fT

This is the transition frequency, which is the frequency at which the current gain of the device falls to unity with the device operated in the common emitter mode. As with an operational amplifier, this also determines the bandwidth that can be obtained at higher voltage gains, although other factors may limit the bandwidth to a figure substantially less than the fT figure would suggest is possible. Most silicon transistors (except power types) have quite high fT figures, and this is not a parameter that is usually of major importance for small or medium power audio stages.

ICBO

More popularly known as the leakage current, this is the maximum current that will flow with no input bias current applied to the device. This leakage current varies quite significantly with changes in temperature, but for a silicon device it is usually so low as to be insignificant. It can be quite high with germanium types though, and these usually require more complex bias circuits in order to guarantee satisfactory results.

VCE(sat)

Often just called the 'saturation' voltage, this is the minimum collector voltage for a given base and collector current. Strictly speaking it is not the lowest collector voltage that can be achieved since a higher base current will normally produce some slight reduction in the collector voltage. However, the reduction will be too small to be of significance once the transistor has been biased into saturation.

tON

When a base current is applied to a transistor it takes a certain time (tON) for the collector current to rise to the appropriate figure.

tOFF

Similar to the above, but it is the time taken for the collector current to fall to its minimum level when the base bias is removed. Due to storage effects the turn-off time for a device which has been biased into saturation is much longer than the turn-on time.

Amplifying Modes

There are three basic amplifying modes for transistors: the common emitter, common base, and common collector (emitter follower) modes. The common emitter type is probably the most common of these modes, and it is the one which has the most useful characteristics for general use. This mode is shown in Figure 38.

The name 'common emitter' is derived from the fact that the emitter terminal is common to both the input and output signals of the circuit. R2 is the collector load resistor, and R1 provides a base bias to TR1 that results in a collector voltage of about half the supply potential. This is the most basic form of biasing and there are other forms of bias circuit

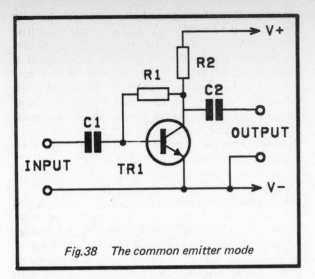

Fig.38 The common emitter mode

incidentally. C1 and C2 provide D.C. blocking at the input and output of the circuit. An input signal has the effect of causing TR1 to conduct more or less heavily, producing variations in the output voltage. The common emitter mode provides input and output impedance figures that are usually not substantially different from one another, and are usually of the order of several kilohms. The voltage gain is quite high, and at audio frequencies a voltage gain of over 40dB (100 times) is easily achieved. This gives a high level of power gain. The signal undergoes an inversion through a common emitter stage.

TR1 is shown as an npn device in Figure 38, but the same configuration will operate properly using a pnp type if the supply is reversed, as shown in Figure 39. The same is true for all three amplifying modes.

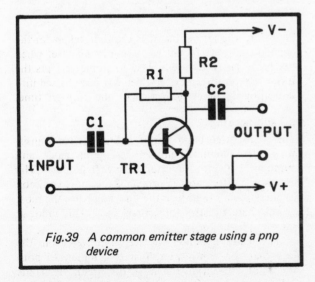

Fig.39 A common emitter stage using a pnp device

Figure 40 shows the common base configuration, which has similarities with the common emitter type. In this case though, the base is decoupled by C1 so that it is held at a fixed voltage and is effectively

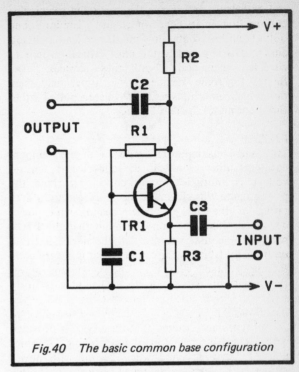

Fig.40 The basic common base configuration

common to both the input and output terminals. An emitter resistor is added so that input signal can be applied to the emitter terminal of the transistor, and here it has the effect of varying the base-emitter voltage, causing variations in the output voltage. The voltage gain is very good in this mode, but the circuit is really acting as a sort of step-up transformer as the input impedance is low (around 200 ohms) and the output impedance is quite high. This gives only a low level of power gain. The input and output of the circuit are in-phase incidentally, and this helps to contribute to the good performance of this mode at high frequencies.

The common collector mode is shown in Figure 41. Although the collector may not seem to be common to both the input and output circuits, or indeed to connect to either of them, the two supply rails are separated by a fixed voltage, and any variation relative to one is a change relative to the other as well. Thus there is an indirect but effective connection from the collector to both the input and output circuits.

This mode has 100% negative feedback, since an increase in the base potential causes TR1 to conduct more heavily, the voltage across load resistor R3 rises, and this increases the emitter voltage which almost completely counteracts the original increase in base voltage. This mode consequently only achieves unity voltage gain, but it provides a high input impedance and a low output impedance. It therefore achieves reasonable power gain, and emitter follower stages are often used as buffer amplifiers to match a high impedance circuit to a low impedance type. There is no inversion through an amplifier of this type.

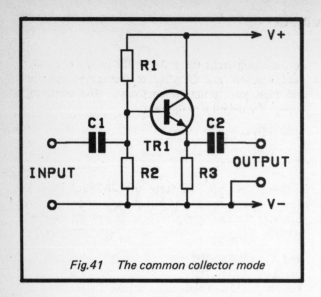

Fig.41   The common collector mode

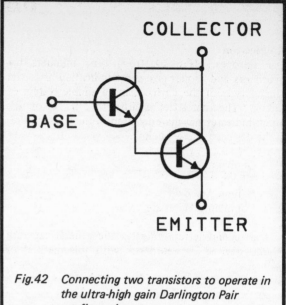

Fig.42   Connecting two transistors to operate in the ultra-high gain Darlington Pair configuration

Darlington Pairs

Transistors are sometimes used in pairs in the way shown in Figure 42; a configuration known as the 'Darlington Pair'. Here the amplified current of one transistor is fed into the base of the second device, giving what is effectively a single transistor with a current gain that is equal to the product of the two individual current gains. In this way an effective hFE figure of many thousands can be obtained. This configuration is most common in high power emitter follower stages, and power Darlington devices are readily available. Low power Darlington devices are also available, but this configuration is generally less effective in low power applications as the first device then operates at a very low current, making it relatively inefficient.

TYPE NUMBERS

Pro Electron

The European (Pro Electron) type numbers for transistors and diodes give some indication as to the general type of the device using a simple system of coding. The first letter is either 'A', 'B', 'C' or 'R', which indicates the material used in the construction of the device, as shown below.

A   Germanium
B   Silicon
C   Galium Arsenide
R   Compound Materials.

The second letter indicates the general category of the device, in accordance with this method of coding:—

A   Small signal diode
B   Rectifier or variable capacitance diode (varicap diode)
C   Small signal audio transistor
D   Power transistor
E   Point contact diode
F   Low power high frequency transistor
G   Diode (oscillator, miscellaneous)
H   Diode (magnetic sensitive)
K   Hall Effect device (open magnetic circuit)
L   High frequency power transistor
M   Hall Effect device (closed magnetic circuit)
N   Opto isolator
P   Diode (radiation sensitive)
Q   Diode (radiation producing)
R   Special purpose device
S   Switching device (transistor or diode)
T   SCR (thyristor or triac)
U   High voltage transistor
X   Rectifier or varicap diode
Y   Power rectifier
Z   Zener diode

As an example of this coding, the popular BC109 transistor is a silicon ('B') small signal audio ('C') device. Some devices which have European type numbers have a third letter, and this indicates that the device has been designed for the more demanding industrial applications (but it does not really seem to be of any particular significance).

Gain Groups

As explained previously, transistors often have very wide gain spread, and this can make it difficult to use them in some kinds of circuit where the unpredictable gain could give equally unpredictable results. Some types, including popular devices such as the BC109, BC179, and the many very similar types, have a suffix letter which indicates that the current gain is within a more restricted range than that for a device which lacks the suffix. The letters normally used as 'A', 'B', and 'C', which represent low, medium and high gain groups respectively. The generally accepted standard is as follows:—

A   110 to 220
B   200 to 450
C   420 to 800

Some 2N types (notably the 2N2926) have a coloured spot on the body of the component which indicates the gain group. These groups are detailed below:—

Red   55 to 100
Orange   90 to 180
Yellow   150 to 300
Green   235 to 470

A few devices have a 'K' or 'L' suffix, and this indicates that the leadout wire arrangement is different to the standard device which does not carry any suffix letter.

The tables that follow shortly give basic but useful data on a wide variety of transistors, and this should be helpful when designing projects or trying to ascertain if a particular device in the spares box is likely to be suitable as a substitute for a specified type. There is only sufficient space available here to accommodate a small fraction of the devices that have been produced, but the lists concentrate on the devices that are readily available to amateur users, and which are popular for use in home constructor designs.

JEDEC Codes

JEDEC (Joint Electronic Device Engineering Councils) is an American organisation, and devices having JEDEC type numbers have their origins in the U.S.A. Devices having JEDEC type numbers are commonly used in projects for the home constructor, and the 2N2926 is an example of this method of coding. These type numbers do not give a great deal of information about the characteristics of the devices, but they do provide some information. The first digit is always a number, and it is the only digit that supplies any significant information about the device. The number is from 1 to 5, and provides the following information:—

1   A diode or other two lead device
2   A bipolar, uni-junction, or field effect transistor, SCR, or triac (i.e. three lead devices)
3   Field effect transistors (four lead types)
4 & 5 Opto-isolators.

The second digit is always an 'N', and this is followed by a number which is up to four digits long. The devices are numbered in sequence as they are registered, and so all this number gives is a rough indication of how new or otherwise a device happens to be. A few devices are available with an 'A' suffix, and this indicates that they are improved versions of the original devices. As such they have a new (and usually substantially different) set of parameters.

JIS Codes

Semiconductors from Japan have JIS (Japanese Industry Standard) type numbers. These have similarities to both the JEDEC and Pro Electron systems, and provide some basic information about each device. Japanese transistors, as yet, have not been used to any great extent in designs for the home constructor, but a few of these devices will be found in most component retailers' semiconductor lists.

The first digit is always a number, and it indicates the number of leads, as detailed below:—

1	Two lead device
2	Three lead device
3	Four lead device.

The next two digits are letters, and they indicate the type of component, as follows:—

SA	PNP transistors and Darlingtons (high frequency)
SB	PNP transistors and Darlingtons (low frequency)
SC	NPN transistors and Darlingtons (high frequency)
SD	NPN transistors and Darlingtons (low frequency)
SE	Diodes
SF	SCRs (thyristors)
SG	Gunn Diodes
SH	Unijunction transistors
SJ	P channel FETs
SK	N channel FETs
SM	SCRs (Triacs)

SQ	Light emitting diodes
SR	Rectifiers
SS	Signal diodes
ST	Avalanche diodes
SV	Varicap and PIN diodes
SZ	Zener diodes

These two letters are followed by a serial number of up to four digits in length. There is occasionally a suffix letter which indicates that the device has been approved by a Japanese organisation ('N' for a device that has been approved by the Japanese broadcasting organisation for example). It is not uncommon for the actual markings on a device to omit the first two digits, but this is not particularly important. The number of leadout wires should be apparent from the device, and the second digit is always an 'S'!

Manufacturers Digits

Some devices are sold under manufacturer's type numbers, and these do not generally give much information about the device. These type numbers always indicate the device's manufacturer, and sometimes indicate the general type of device involved as well. This list details some of the more common prefixes (which are normally followed by the manufacturer's serial number).

MJ	Motorola (metal cased power transistor)
MJE	Motorola (plastic cased power transistor)
MPS	Motorola (plastic cased low power transistor)
MRF	Motorola (high frequency or microwave transistor)
RCA	RCA
RCS	RCS
TIP	Texas Instruments (plastic cased power transistor)
TIPL	Texas Instruments (planar power transistor)
TIS	Texas Instruments (low power transistor)
ZT	Ferranti
ZTX	Ferranti

TRANSISTOR CHARACTERISTIC TABLES

Small to Medium Power Audio Transistors						
Device	*Type*	*VCEO*	*hFE*	*PTOT (mW)*	*IC (mA)*	*Case*
AC127	npn (G)	12	50 typ.	340	500	TO1
AC128	pnp (G)	16	60–175	700	1000	TO1
AC176	npn (G)	18	50–250	1000	1000	TO1
BC107	npn	45	110–450	300	100	TO18
BC108	npn	20	110–800	300	100	TO18
BC109	npn	20	110–800	300	100	TO18
BC117	npn	120	40 typ.	500	20	TO39
BC142	npn	60	20 min.	800	800	TO39
BC143	pnp	60	25 min.	800	800	TO39
BC169C	npn	20	650 typ.	300	50	TO92
BC171	npn	45	110–450	300	100	TO92a
BC177	pnp	45	125–500	300	100	TO18
BC178	pnp	25	125–500	300	100	TO18
BC179	pnp	25	240–500	300	100	TO18
BC182L	npn	50	100–480	300	200	TO92
BC183L	npn	30	100–850	300	200	TO92
BC184L	npn	30	125 min.	300	200	TO92
BC212L	pnp	50	60–300	300	200	TO92
BC213L	pnp	30	80–400	300	200	TO92
BC214L	pnp	30	140–600	300	200	TO92
BC239	npn	45	290 typ.	360	100	TO92h
BC327	pnp	45	100–600	625	500	TO92b
BC337	npn	45	100–600	625	500	TO92b
BC441	npn	60	40–250	1000	2000	TO39
BC461	pnp	60	40–250	1000	2000	TO39
BC547	npn	45	520 typ.	500	100	TO92a

Device	Type	VCEO	hFE	PTOT (mW)	IC (mA)	Case
BC548	npn	30	520 typ.	500	100	TO92a
BC549	npn	30	520 typ.	500	100	TO92a
BC557	pnp	45	240 typ.	500	100	TO92a
BC558	pnp	30	240 typ.	500	100	TO92a
BC559	pnp	30	240 typ.	500	100	TO92a
BC650	npn	30	750 typ.	625	100	TO92b
BCY70	pnp	40	300 typ.	360	200	TO18
BCY71	pnp	45	100–400	360	200	TO18
BFX29	pnp	60	125 typ.	600	600	TO5
BFX30	pnp	65	90 typ.	600	600	TO5
BFX84	npn	60	110 typ.	800	1000	TO5
BFX85	npn	60	140 typ.	800	1000	TO5
BFX87	pnp	50	125 typ.	600	600	TO5
BFX88	pnp	40	125 typ.	600	600	TO5
BFY50	npn	35	110 typ.	800	1000	TO5
BFY51	npn	30	125 typ.	800	1000	TO5
BFY52	npn	20	142 typ.	800	1000	TO5
ZTX107	npn	50	240 typ.	300	100	E-lne
ZTX108	npn	30	240 typ.	300	100	E-lne
ZTX109	npn	30	410 typ.	300	100	E-lne
ZTX300	npn	25	150 typ.	300	500	E-lne
ZTX500	pnp	25	150 typ.	300	500	E-lne
ZTX650	npn	45	200 typ.	1500	2000	E-lne
ZTX651	npn	60	200 typ.	1500	2000	E-lne
ZTX750	pnp	45	200 typ.	1500	2000	E-lne
ZTX751	pnp	60	200 typ.	1500	2000	E-lne
2N697	npn	40	75 typ.	600	500	TO5
2N706	npn	20	20 min.	300	100	TO18

Small to Medium Power Audio Transistors – *continued*

	Small to Medium Power Audio Transistors – *continued*					
Device	*Type*	*VCEO*	*hFE*	*PTOT (mW)*	*IC (mA)*	*Case*
2N1711	npn	30	200 typ.	800	1000	TO5
2N1893	npn	80	80 typ.	800	500	TO5
2N2219	npn	30	200 typ.	800	800	TO5
2N2905	pnp	40	100–300	600	600	TO5
2N2906	pnp	40	80 typ.	400	600	TO18
2N2907	pnp	40	200 typ.	400	600	TO18
2N2926	npn	18	55–435	200	100	TO98
2N3702	pnp	25	60–300	300	200	TO92
2N3703	pnp	30	30–150	300	200	TO92
2N3704	npn	30	100–300	360	800	TO92
2N3705	npn	30	50–150	360	800	TO92
2N3706	npn	20	315 typ.	360	800	TO92
2N3707	npn	30	250 typ.	250	30	TO92
2N3708	npn	30	360 typ.	250	30	TO92
2N3711	npn	30	420 typ.	250	30	TO92
2N3903	npn	40	100 typ.	300	200	TO92b
2N3904	npn	40	100–300	310	200	TO92b
2N3905	pnp	40	50 typ.	310	200	TO92b
2N3906	pnp	40	100–300	310	200	TO92b

The gain figures are mostly quoted at 1 or 2 milliamps for small types, and a much higher current (around 100 milliamps for medium power types). The 2N3707 is designed for low current applications, and the gain is quoted at 100 microamps. The BC109, BC169, BC179, BC549, BC559, and BC650 are high gain low noise audio devices. The 2N697, 2N706, 2N2906, 2N2907, 2N2219, 2N2905, ZTX650, ZTX651, ZTX750, and ZTX751 are all high speed switching devices.

Small and Medium Power Radio Frequency Transistors							
Device	Type	VCEO	hFE	PTOT (mW)	IC (mA)	fT (MHz)	Case
AF127	pnp (G)	20	150 (hfe)	60	10	75	TO72
AF239	pnp (G)	15	30 typ.	60	10	700	TO72A
BF115	npn	30	40 typ.	145	30	230	TO72A
BF173	npn	25	38 typ.	260	25	350	TO72A
BF180	npn	20	13 typ.	150	200	325	TO72
BF182	npn	20	75 typ.	145	30	325	TO72
BF184	npn	20	75 typ.	145	30	150	TO72A
BF185	npn	20	34 typ.	145	30	110	TO72A
BF194	npn	20	67 typ.	250	30	130	X09A
BF195	npn	20	36 typ.	250	30	100	X09A
BF196	npn	30	27 typ.	250	25	200	X09A
BF197	npn	20	38 typ.	250	25	275	X09A
BF200	npn	20	13 typ.	150	20	325	TO72
BF254	npn	20	115 typ.	220	30	260	TO92ZA
BF255	npn	20	67 typ.	220	30	260	TO92ZA
BF257	npn	160	25 typ.	500	100	55	TO39
BF258	npn	250	25 typ.	800	100	55	TO39
BF259	npn	300	25 typ.	500	100	90	TO39
BF337	npn	225	20 typ.	800	100	80	TO39
BF420	npn	300	40 min.	830	25	60	TO92A
BF421	pnp	300	40 min.	830	25	60	TO92A
BFR39	npn	80	50 typ.	800	1000	100	TO92A
BFR40	npn	60	75 typ.	800	1000	100	TO92A
BFR41	npn	50	100 typ.	800	1000	100	TO92A
BFR79	pnp	80	50 typ.	800	1000	100	TO92A
BFR80	pnp	60	75 typ.	800	1000	100	TO92A
BFR81	pnp	50	100 typ.	800	1000	100	TO92A
BFY90	npn	15	52 typ.	200	50	1850	TO72
BSX20	npn	15	80 typ.	360	500	500	TO18
2N2222A	npn	40	200 typ.	500	800	300	TO18
2N2369A	npn	15	40 min.	360	200	500	TO18
2N3866	npn	30	105 typ.	5000	400	700	TO5

Power Devices							
Device	Type	VCEO	hFE	PTOT (W)	IC (A)	fT (MHz)	Case
AD161	npn (G)	20	80 typ.	4	1	1	SO55
AD162	pnp (G)	20	50 typ.	6	1	1	SO55
BD131	npn	45	20 min.	15	3	60	TO126
BD132	pnp	45	20 min.	15	3	60	TO126
BD135	npn	45	40–250	12.5	1.5	50	TO126
BD136	pnp	45	40–250	12.5	1.5	75	TO126
BD139	npn	80	100 typ.	8	1	250	TO126
BD140	pnp	80	100 typ.	8	1	75	TO126
BD437	npn	45	40 typ.	36	4	3	TO126
BD438	pnp	45	40 typ.	36	4	3	TO126
BD679	npn (D)	80	2200 typ.	40	6	0.06	P1b
BD680	pnp (D)	80	2200 typ.	40	6	0.06	P1b
BD711	npn	100	25 typ.	75	12	3	P1b
BD712	pnp	100	25 typ.	75	12	3	P1b
BU205	npn	1500	2 min.	10	2.5	7.5	TO3
BU208	npn	1500	2.25 min.	12.5	5	7	TO3
BU326A	npn	400	15 typ.	60	6	6	TO3
MJ2501	pnp (D)	80	1000 typ.	150	10	1	TO3
MJ2955	npn	60	45 typ.	150	15	4	TO3
MJ3001	npn	80	1000 typ.	150	10	1	TO3
MJE340	npn	300	150 typ.	20	0.5	20	TO126
MJE350	pnp	300	150 typ.	20	0.5	20	TO126
TIP31A	npn	60	25 typ.	40	3	3	P1b
TIP32A	pnp	60	25 typ.	40	3	3	P1b
TIP33A	npn	60	75 typ.	80	10	3	P3c
TIP34A	pnp	60	75 typ.	80	10	3	P3c
TIP41A	npn	60	50 typ.	65	5	3	P1b
TIP42A	pnp	60	50 typ.	65	5	3	P1b

Power Devices – *continued*							
Device	*Type*	*VCEO*	*hFE*	*PTOT (W)*	*IC (A)*	*fT (MHz)*	*Case*
TIP110	npn (D)	60	500 min.	50	2	–	P1b
TIP115	pnp (D)	60	500 min.	50	2	–	P1b
TIP121	npn (D)	80	1000 min.	65	5	1	P1b
TIP122	npn (D)	100	5000 typ.	65	5	5	P1b
TIP126	pnp (D)	80	1000 min.	65	5	1	P1b
TIP127	pnp (D)	100	5000 typ.	65	5	5	P1b
TIP2955	pnp	70	45 typ.	90	15	2	P3c
TIP3055	npn	70	45 typ.	90	15	2	P3c
2N3054	npn	55	25 typ.	29	4	1	TO66
2N3055	npn	60	45 typ.	115	15	0.8	TO3
2N3372	npn	60	30 typ.	150	20	0.8	TO3
2N3773	npn	140	40 typ.	150	16	0.2	TO3

Note that the VCEO figures for the BU205 and BU208 are non-repetitive peak values. In the 'Type' column, a 'G' indicates a germanium device and a 'D' indicates a power Darlington type.

Note that many power devices have quite low fT figures, and in some cases may not even provide full gain over the entire audio band.

Field Effect Devices

Originally the only type of field effect transistor was the junction gate (Jfet) type, but these have now been joined by dual gate MOSFETs, and more recently by VMOS and power MOSFETs (also known as HMOS devices). All these devices can operate in amplifying modes that are analogous to the common emitter, common base, and common collector modes. However, the terminals of field effect devices are the source, gate, and drain, and the amplifying modes are respectively the common source, common gate, and common drain (source follower) types.

Field effect devices differ from bipolar devices most radically in that they are essentially voltage rather than current operated devices. They have extremely high input resistances that are usually around a thousand megohms for the Jfet type, and often very much greater than this for the MOS varieties. The input impedance is similarly high at low frequencies, but it reduces vastly at high frequencies due to the input capacitance of typically about 10pF.

Jfet devices differ from bipolar types in that they are depletion mode transistors rather than enhancement types. In other words, the device is normally switched on, and it requires a reverse bias in order to bring it into a section of its transfer characteristic that is suitable for linear amplification. The standard Jfet common source amplifier configuration is shown in Figure 43. As TR1 conducts readily between its drain and source terminals, this gives a strong current flow through R2, TR1, and R3. This gives a voltage across R3 which results in TR1's source terminal going positive of its gate terminal, which is tied to earth by gate bias resistor R1. This gives the reverse bias required in order to give linear amplification, and is essentially the same as the common cathode mode of amplification and biasing used in valve circuits. Of course, FETs are not distortion-free, although the levels of distortion produced prior to the addition of any negative feedback are generally lower than those from bipolar circuits.

Whereas Jfet devices are used in both audio and radio frequency applications, dual gate MOSFETs are

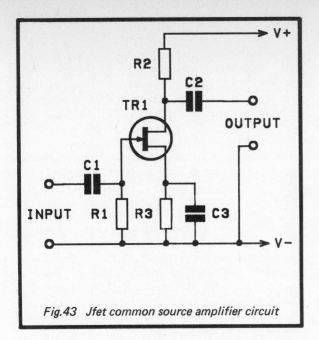

Fig.43 Jfet common source amplifier circuit

rarely used at low frequencies. Their gain and general level of performance at high frequencies is extremely good, and the second gate terminal increases their versatility. Figure 44 shows the basic common source configuration for a dual gate MOSFET device. This is much the same as the Jfet circuit described previously, with the gate 1 terminal being reverse biased in exactly the same way. R3 connects the gate 2 terminal to the TR1's source so that it has zero bias. A crucial factor in many circuits is the ability to vary the gain from gate 1 to the output of the device by altering the gate 2 bias voltage. As shown in Figure 44 the circuit exhibits full gain, but by reducing the gate 2 bias voltage the gain can be substantially reduced. This has two main practical applications, and one of these is to permit easy

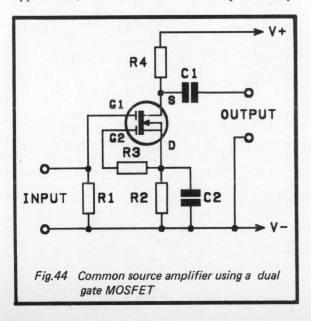

Fig.44 Common source amplifier using a dual gate MOSFET

application of A.G.C. (automatic gain control) to an amplifier which is based on a dual gate MOSFET. The other is to apply the output from an oscillator to the gate 2 terminal so that the circuit operates as a mixer rather than an amplifier. Here we are talking in terms of a mixer of the type used in superheterodyne receivers rather than an audio type mixer, and it is really a form of modulator.

VMOS and power MOSFETs have similar characteristics, and are both power devices, although some VMOS devices are only medium power transistors rather than fully blown power types. Normal FET devices have "on" resistances that are usually in the region of 100 to 500 ohms, which obviously makes them totally unsuitable for high or even medium power applications. VMOS and power MOSFETs have much lower "on" resistances of about 2 ohms or less, and they can handle quite high currents (several amps in some cases). They are enhancement mode devices (i.e. normally cut off and switched on by a forward bias), but they are voltage rather than current operated devices, like other FET types.

They have a number of advantages over bipolar power devices, one of which is their extremely high gain. An input signal of a few volts at a negligble current can be made to switch an output current of as much as a few amps. They also have relatively fast switching speeds and have total freedom from secondary breakdown. They do not suffer from thermal runaway either. This is where a transistor becomes hot when dissipating a fairly high power, which results in it conducting more heavily, dissipating more power, becoming heated and conducting even more heavily, and so on. This can eventually lead to the destruction of the device. This effect can not occur with VMOS and power MOSFETs as they either have a negative temperature coefficient, or one which starts as a mildly positive coefficient but which changes to a slightly negative type at a low to medium current. This tends to stabilise the current rather than encourage thermal runaway.

VMOS and power MOSFETs are not without their disadvantages, and have not become as popular as was expected when they were originally introduced. One problem is that they are probably slightly more easily damaged than are bipolar power devices, and in many circuit configurations they are somewhat less efficient. Probably the main drawback is that they are still relatively expensive.

Parameters

Field effect devices are sufficiently different from bipolar types for them to have an almost completely different set of parameters, although I suppose that most of these have fairly close bipolar equivalents. A brief explanation of the more important FET parameters follows.

VDS

The maximum permissible drain to source voltage (roughly equivalent to VCEO for bipolar types).

VDG

The maximum permissible drain to gate voltage (roughly equivalent to VCBO for bipolar transistors).

VGS

The maximum permissible gate to source voltage (roughly equivalent to VEBO for bipolar devices, but the same avalanche effect is not produced, although some VMOS types are static protected by a 15 volt zener diode).

Vp

Often termed the 'pinch-off' voltage, this is the reverse gate to source bias voltage needed to cut off a depletion mode device.

PT

Same as PTOT for a bipolar device (i.e. the maximum power rating for the device).

fT

Same as fT for a bipolar device, but it is the unity gain bandwidth in the common source mode rather than the common emitter mode).

Ciss

The common source input capacitance.

gm

The small signal common source transconductance. This is roughly equivalent to hFE for a bipolar transistor, and is the FET gain measurement. It is a measurement of how much the drain current varies with changes in the gate voltage. A change of (say) 8mA per volt would be given in a data sheet as a gm of 8mmho (with 'mmho' being a milli-mho, or 0.001mho). The gm formula of current divided by voltage is the opposite of that used to calculate resistance using Ohm's Law, and the term 'mho' is supposedly derived from this (being ohm spelled backwards).

VGS(th)

This parameter only applies to enhancement mode devices, and it is the gate turn-on threshold voltage. In other words, it is the forward gate bias voltage at which the device starts to conduct significantly.

IDSS

This is the enhancement mode FET equivalent to leakage in a bipolar transistor, and it is the drain current that flows with zero gate voltage. Even for power devices this is usually very low, being a few microamps at most, and is therefore insignificant in practice.

IGSS

The gate body leakage current, which is the gate current that flows for a given gate voltage. With the very high input resistance of FET devices this is usually very low indeed (about 2 nanoamps), but can be as much as a few microamps for power types under worst case conditions.

ID

The maximum permissible drain current (generally only specified in this form for power devices).

IDss

A depletion mode FET parameter, this is the drain current that flows with zero gate to source voltage. From this parameter and the gm figure it is possible to calculate the drain current for other gate voltages, but the tolerances on these figures are generally quite wide with the minimum IDss figure often being only about one-tenth of the maximum figure. This tends to make reliable biasing of depletion mode FETs a difficult task.

ton

This is the switch on time for the device.

toff

This is the switch on time for the component. Unlike bipolar devices, the turn on and turn off delay times of FETs are often the same.

RDS

The drain to source resistance with the device fully switched on.

VDS(on)

The power FET equivalent of saturation voltage, this is the drain to source voltage with the device turned on and passing a specified current.

The range of readily available field effect devices is much more restricted than the broad selection of obtainable bipolar types. The two tables following give brief details for most of the devices that are available through retail outlets.

Unijunctions

Although unijunction transistors were very popular at one time, they have been largely superseded by integrated circuits and other devices, and are little used these days. In fact many of these devices are now obsolete. They have little in common with ordinary bipolar or field effect transistors, with their two base terminals and single emitter. They are normally used in the relaxation oscillator configuration of Figure 45. Here C1 charges up by way of R1 until a certain voltage is reached, and then TR1 fires and rapidly discharges C1. When C1 is almost fully discharged TR1 switches off again, C1 commences to charge again, and so on. This gives a high impedance

FET CHARACTERISTIC TABLES

Small Signal FETs						
Device	Type	VDS	gm (mmho)	PT (mW)	IDss (max)	Case
BF244	N-Jfet	30	4.5 typ.	360	25	TO92d
BF244B	N-Jfet	30	3—6.5	360	25	TO92d
BFW10	N-Jfet	30	3.2 typ.	300	20	TO12
MPF102	N-Jfet	25	1.6 typ.	200	20	TO92c
2N3819	N-Jfet	25	2—6.5	200	20	TO92d
2N3820	P-Jfet	20	0.8—5	200	15	TO92d
2N3823E	N-Jfet	30	1.8 min.	250	20	TO106f
2N4303	N-Jfet	30	2 min.	300	10	TO106f
2N5457	N-Jfet	25	1—5	200	5	TO92c
2N5458	N-Jfet	25	1.5—5.5	200	9	TO92c
2N5459	N-Jfet	25	2—6	200	16	TO92c
3N140	DG-MOS	20	10 typ.	330	30	TO72f
3SK88	DG-MOS	20	17 typ.	200	6	37
3SK124	DG-GAS	10	30 typ.	200	40	37
40673	DG-MOS	20	12 typ.	330	35	TO72f

In the 'Type' column 'N' is for N channel, 'P' is for P channel, 'Jfet' is a junction gate FET, 'DG-MOS' is a dual gate MOSFET, and 'DG-GAS' is a dual gate galium arsenide device. The BFW10 is a low noise device for low frequency applications, and the 3SK124 is a very low noise high frequency device (noise figure of 1.3dB at 900MHz).

Power FETs						
Device	Type	VDS	gm (mmho)	PT (W)	ID (max A)	Case
VN10KM	N-VMOS	60	200 typ.	1	0.5	TO92d
VN46AF	N-VMOS	40	250 typ.	12.5	2	P1c
VN66AF	N-VMOS	60	250 typ.	12.5	2	P1c
VN67AF	N-VMOS	60	250 typ.	15	2	P1c
VN88AF	N-VMOS	80	250 typ.	12.5	2	P1c
2SJ48	P-PMOS	120	1000 typ.	100	7	TO3v
2SJ49	P-PMOS	140	1000 typ.	100	7	TO3v

Power FETs – *continued*						
Device	Type	VDS	gm (mmho)	PT (W)	ID (max A)	Case
2SJ50	P-PMOS	160	1000 typ.	100	7	TO3v
2SJ83	P-PMOS	160	1000 typ.	100	7	FPACK
2SK133	N-PMOS	120	1000 typ.	100	7	TO3v
2SK134	N-PMOS	140	1000 typ.	100	7	TO3v
2SK135	N-PMOS	160	1000 typ.	100	7	TO3v
2SK227	N-PMOS	160	1000 typ.	100	7	FPACK

In the 'Type' column 'N' indicates an N channel device, 'P' indicates a P channel type, 'VMOS' indicates a VMOS device, and 'PMOS' is for a power MOSFET.

non-linear sawtooth waveform at the emitter of TR1, and low impedance pulse signals at the base 1 and base 2 terminals.

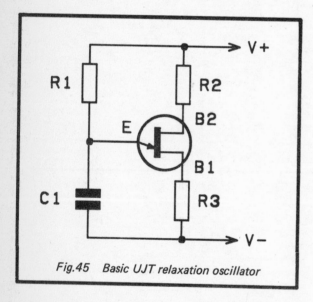

Fig.45   Basic UJT relaxation oscillator

The main parameters for these transistors are detailed below:—

PTOT
Maximum power dissipation.

RBB
The static base 1 to base 2 resistance.

n
The intrinsic stand-off ratio. A unijunction under static conditions is effectively a pair of resistors connected in series between the two base terminals, with the emitter connecting to the junction of these two resistors via a silicon diode. The intrinsic stand-off ratio is the base 1 to emitter resistance divided by the base 1 to base 2 resistance. The device 'fires' when the silicon diode at the emitter terminal becomes forward biased, and this voltage depends on the supply voltage and the intrinsic stand-off ratio. It is approximately equal to the supply voltage multiplied by the intrinsic stand-off ratio, plus about 0.6 volts to allow for the forward threshold voltage of the diode junction.

VBB
The maximum permissible base 1 to base 2 voltage.

VEB20
The maximum permissible reverse voltage from the emitter to base 2.

IP
The peak point current, which is the minimum emitter current needed to trigger the device. This determines the maximum usable value for the timing resistor in the relaxation oscillator circuit.

IV
This is the valley point current, which is the minimum emitter current that will keep the device in the triggered state.

IE
The maximum peak emitter current rating.

Brief data for a few common unijunction transistors follows.

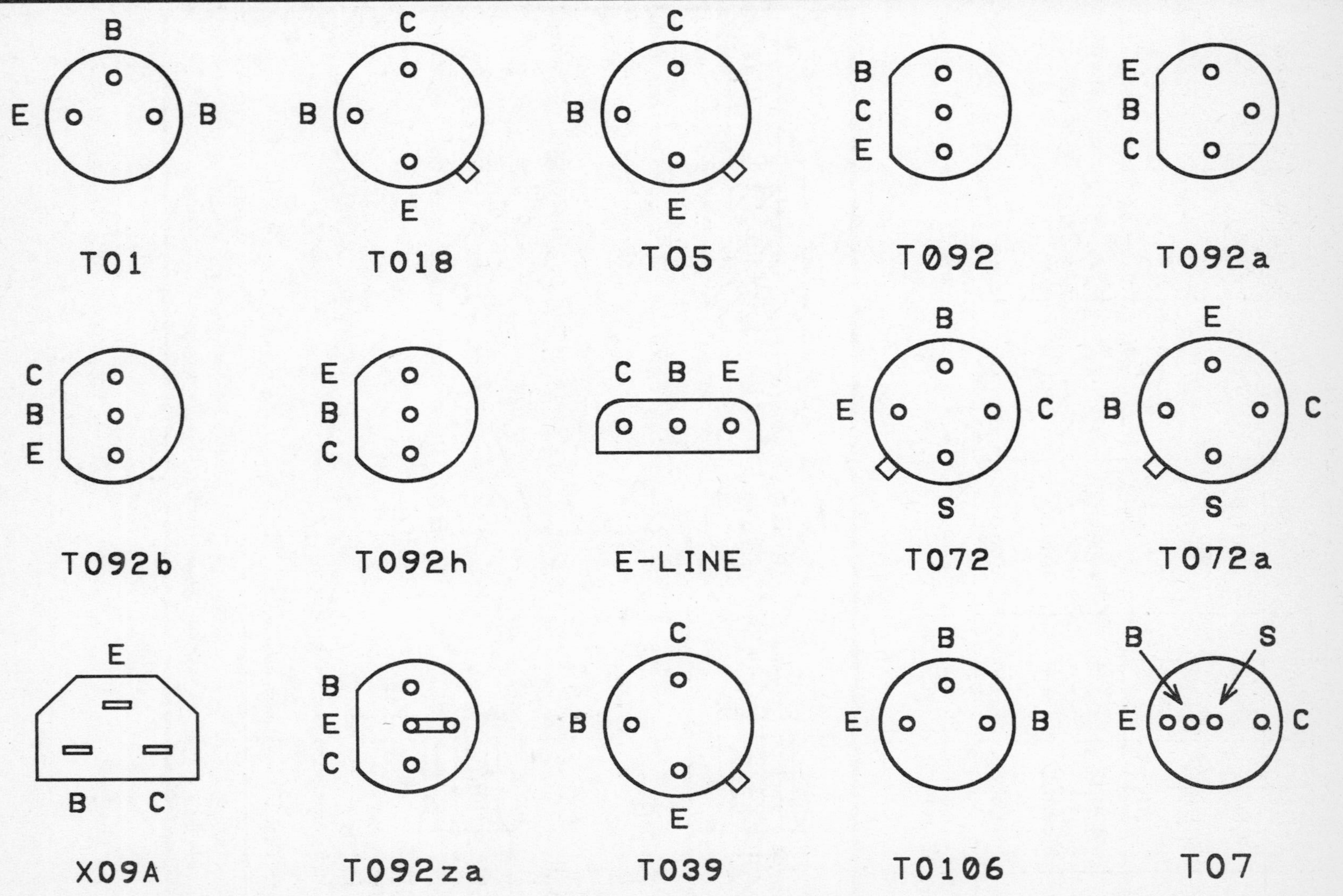

TO1   TO18   TO5   TO92   TO92a

TO92b   TO92h   E-LINE   TO72   TO72a

XO9A   TO92za   TO39   TO106   TO7

Fig.46 Small signal transistor leadout details

61

UNIJUNCTION CHARACTERISTICS TABLE

Device	VBB	VEB20	RBB (k)	n	IP (μA)	Case
TIS43	35	30	4 – 9.1	0.55 – 0.82	5	TO92e
2N2646	35	30	4.7 – 9.1	0.56 – 0.75	5	TO18u
2N4871	35	30	4 – 9.1	0.7 – 0.85	5	TO92g

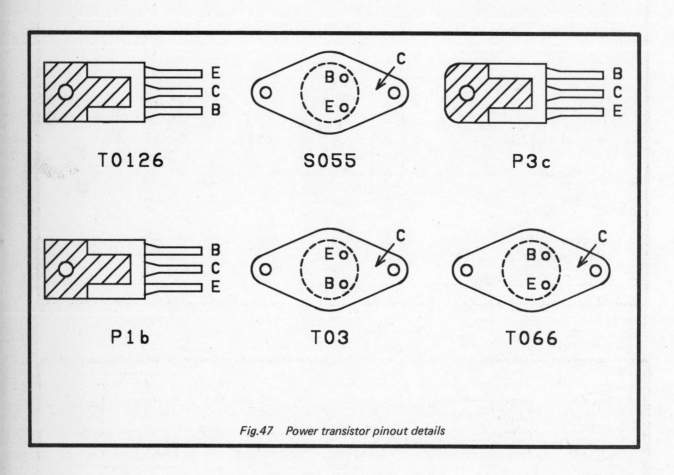

Fig.47   Power transistor pinout details

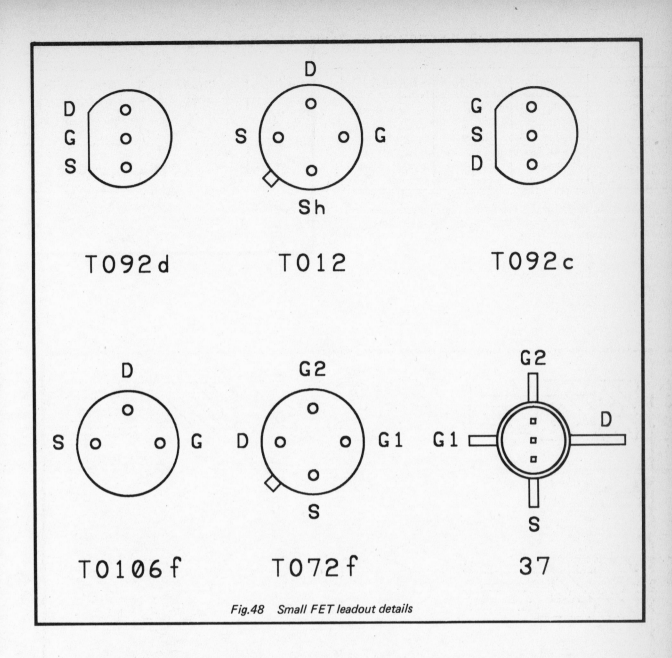

Fig.48   Small FET leadout details

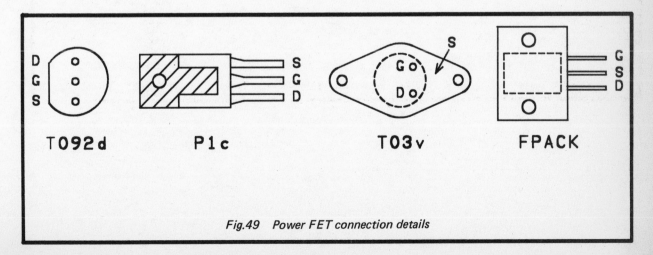

Fig.49   Power FET connection details

A range of transistor leadout diagrams are provided in Figures 46 to 50, which are respectively small signal bipolar, power bipolar, small signal FET, power FET, and unijunction transistor base views. Note that all the diagrams show the devices looking onto the underside, including the power transistor leadout diagrams. Some transistor encapsulations and leadout arrangements are known by names other than those used here, and the names are intended only for use in conjunction with the data tables provided in this publication. Some devices may be available in more than one encapsulation (I have, for example, come across 2N3819 Jfets in both TO92 and TO106 encapsulations).

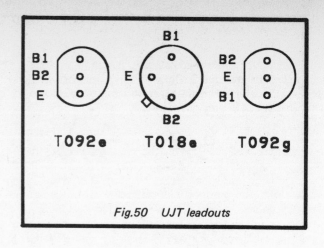

Fig.50   UJT leadouts

Several types of semiconductor device have been covered in previous sections of this book, but here we will cover the main types which have not been encompassed in previous sections.

Diodes

Rectifiers were covered in the section dealing with power supplies, but there are other forms of diode in common use which have not been dealt with up to now. The most common of these are the small signal diodes which fall into two main categories; silicon and germanium types. The silicon type have the advantage of extremely high reverse leakage currents, but have the disadvantage of requiring a forward bias of about 0.6 volts before they will begin to conduct significantly. Germanium diodes have a much smaller forward voltage drop, especially at low pass currents, and this makes them much better for use where very small signals must be rectified (as in A.M. detector stages for example). They have much higher reverse leakage currents though, which makes them less appropriate to some applications. Also, germanium devices in general are more vulnerable to damage by excessive heat than are silicon types, and due care has to be exercised when soldering these devices into circuit.

The polarity of a diode is normally indicated by a band around the cathode (+) end of the body. I have encountered one or two diodes with the band at the other end, but I would assume this to be due to faulty marking rather than some diodes being intentionally marked in this way. Some devices now seem to have several bands around the body of the component, and these can be a little confusing. The bands are apparently some form of colour coding, and in the case of the popular 1N4148 for instance, the '4148' part of the type number is marked in the standard resistor 'digit' colour codes (i.e. yellow – brown – yellow – grey). With this type of marking the first band in the sequence indicates the cathode end of the component, and this band is generally about twice as broad as the others. Thus, even if you do not know the colour coding used on a particular device, the broader band will still usually indicate the polarity.

Figure 51 should help with any problems in determining the correct polarity for a diode. For most purposes the 1N4148 diode is suitable where a silicon diode is called for, and an OA91 will suffice where a germanium type is required. However, other types are available, and brief specifications for these are provided in the table on page 66.

Schottky diodes are special low voltage drop silicon devices with very high switching speeds (as used in the 74LSXX series of logic devices). The forward voltage drop is generally only about half that for an ordinary silicon type. The gold bonded type is a fast, low voltage drop germanium type. In the table on page 66 'G' indicates a germanium type, and 'S' indicates a silicon device.

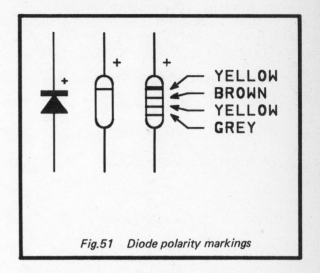

Fig.51 Diode polarity markings

Varicap Diodes

It is a characteristic of all diodes that when they have a certain amount of capacitance across their terminals, and when they are reverse biased this capacitance decreases. Variable capacitance ('Varicap') diodes exploit this effect to enable voltage control of L-C tuning circuits in radio receivers. The basic tuning set-up shown in Figure 52(a), but in practice the twin diode back-to-back configuration of Figure 52(b) is probably more common. Note though, that with the twin diode circuit the capacitance of the two diodes is just half that of the individual capacitance as they are series connected. The twin diode arrangement is less prone to overloading and the consequent problems of the distortion that this would produce.

The early variable capacitance diodes were only intended for use in V.H.F. and U.H.F. equipment, and were of little use for much else as they had low capacitance values with small capacitance swings. These days there are also high capacity types with large capacitance swings, suitable for use in applications such as medium and long wave receivers. Basic data for a few varicap diodes is provided in the Varicap Diode Characteristics Table following, and connection details for some of these components are provided in Figure 53. Many of these devices have ordinary diode style encapsulations and details of these types are not included in Figure 53.

SCRs

A silicon controlled rectifier (SCR) is a switching device, and normally, like an ordinary rectifier, it conducts between its anode and cathode terminals

DIODE CHARACTERISTICS TABLE

Device	Type	PIV	IF (max)	Application
AA119	G Point contract	45V	35 mA	AM/FM detector
BA244	S	20V	100 mA	Fast switching
BAR28	Schottky barrier	70V	–	Fast – low V drop
BAX13	S Whiskerless	50V	75 mA	Fast switching
BAX16	S Whiskerless	150V	200 mA	General purpose
BY206	S Double Diff	350V	400 mA	Switching PSUs
HSCH1001	Schottky barrier	60V	15 mA	Fast – low V drop
OA47	G Gold bonded	25V	110 mA	Low V drop switching
OA90	G Point contact	30V	10 mA	AM/FM detector
OA91	G Point contact	115V	50 mA	General purpose
OA95	G Point contact	115V	50 mA	General purpose
OA200	S Alloy junction	50V	80 mA	General purpose
OA202	S Alloy junction	150V	40 mA	General purpose
ZS120	S Alloy junction	50V	250 mA	General purpose
1N914	S Whiskerless	100V	75 mA	Fast switching
1N914B	S Whiskerless	75V	75 mA	Low V drop
1N916	S Whiskerless	50V	250 mA	Low cap. switching
1N4148	S Whiskerless	100V	75 mA	Fast switching
1S921	S Diffused	100V	200 mA	General purpose

VARICAP DIODE CHARACTERISTICS TABLE

Device	Type	VR (max)	C/V	C/V
BA102	Single	20V	40p/2V	10p/10V
BB105B	Single	28V	11.5p/3V	2.2p/25V
BB212	Dual	12V	550p/0.5V	17p/8V
MV2108	Single	30V	27p/4V	
MVAM115	Single	18V	300p/3V	27p/15V

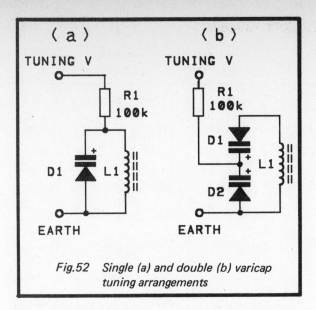

Fig.52   Single (a) and double (b) varicap tuning arrangements

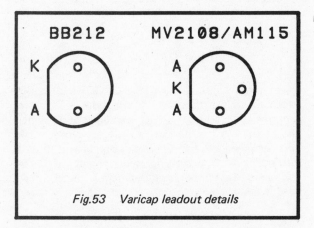

Fig.53   Varicap leadout details

when they are forward biased. However, an SCR has an additional terminal called the 'gate', and it is only when this is forward biased with respect to the cathode the device is triggered into conduction. The voltage drop through the device is somewhat higher than that through a silicon rectifier, being about twice as high at around 1.2 to 2 volts. Once an SCR, or thyristor as they are popularly known, has been triggered, it will remain in a state of conduction until the anode to cathode current falls below a certain level, even if the gate bias is removed. The gate pulse generally only needs to be quite short, with a $1\mu s$ pulse usually being sufficient to trigger the device properly. Note that there are a few special thyristors called 'gate turn-off' types where it is possible to switch them off via the gate terminal. A brief explanation of some SCR parameters is provided below.

Vr
This is the maximum reverse voltage that should be applied to the device (i.e. the maximum voltage with the anode fed from the negative supply and the cathode fed from the positive supply). This is something that is only likely to be of importance if the device is fed from an A.C. supply, as it is otherwise unlikely that it would receive a reverse voltage.

Vf
Similar to above, but it is the maximum permissible forward voltage, and it is this rating that normally determines the maximum supply voltage that can be used for the device. Where the component is being fed from an A.C. or half wave rectified D.C. supply, bear in mind that the peak voltage is about 1.42 times higher than the R.M.S. value. The peak value must not exceed Vf. For this reason it is normal for 400 volt devices to be used in applications where a 240 volt A.C. mains load must be controlled (the peak mains voltage being about 340 volts).

If
The maximum continuous (or R.M.S.) current which the device can pass between its anode and cathode terminals.

Vg
In order to give an adequate gate current to trigger the device a gate voltage above a certain level will be needed. This is simply the maximum gate voltage that will be needed to trigger the device. It is generally under 2 volts.

Ig
This is the maximum gate current that is required in order to guarantee triggering of the component. Some older types require as much as 20 to 30 milliamps, but many of the more recent types will trigger at only about one-tenth of this level, and some types are guaranteed to trigger at under 1 milliamp.

Ihm
Known as the 'holding' or 'hold-on' current, this is the maximum current that will be needed in order to hold the device in the on state. In other words, a lower current flow than this figure is guaranteed to switch the device off.

Vfm
This is simply the maximum forward voltage drop through the device.

Thyristors are not always sold under particular type numbers, and are sometimes sold simply as types having particular Vf and If figures. These will suffice for most purposes, but obviously they might have other parameters that are unsuitable for a given circuit. Where a particular device is specified it is advisable to use the specified type rather than a component that is something of an unknown quantity. The following table gives basic data on some popular devices.

THYRISTOR CHARACTERISTICS TABLE

Device	Vr (V)	If (A)	Ig (mA)	Vg (V)	Ihm (mA)	Case
BT109	500	4	10	2	3	PLAS
BT149B	200	0.64	0.2	0.8	5	TO92a
TAG84	600	0.64	0.2	0.8	5	TO92a
C106D	400	2.5	0.2	0.8	3	PLAS
C106M	600	2.5	0.2	0.8	3	PLAS
C116D	400	5	20	1.5	35	PLAS
C126D	400	7.5	30	1.5	35	PLAS
2N1599	400	1	10	3	—	TO5

Pinout details for a range of thyristors are shown in Figure 54. Figure 55 shows leadout details for two styles of TO92 encapsulated thyristors.

Triacs

Triacs are another form of silicon controlled rectifier, but they are a bidirectional type. They can therefore be used to control A.C. loads as they conduct in both directions once triggered. Also, they can be triggered by a positive or a negative gate bias. Data from some common triacs is provided in the table on page 69, and Figure 56 provides pinout details for these devices.

Diacs

A diac is a bidirectional trigger diode which can be used to trigger thyristor or triacs in A.C. power control applications. A diac is actually quite similar to a triac, but it is designed to trigger when a certain threshold voltage (usually about 30 volts) is exceeded rather than being triggered by way of a gate terminal. Therefore it is only a two-terminal device, and it can be connected into circuit either way round.

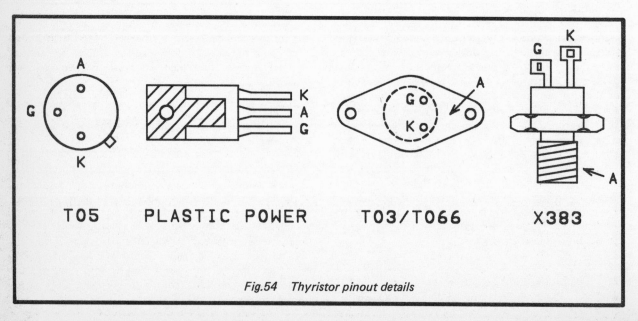

Fig.54   Thyristor pinout details

TRIAC CHARACTERISTICS TABLE

Device	Vr (V)	If (A)	Ig (mA)	Vg (V)	Ihm (mA)	Case
C206D	400	3	5	2	30	PLAS
C226D	400	8	50	2.5	60	PLAS
C236D	400	12	50	2.5	50	PLAS
C246D	400	16	50	2.5	50	PLAS
SC146D	400	10	50	2.5	75	PLAS
2N6073	400	4	30	2.5	70	PLAS

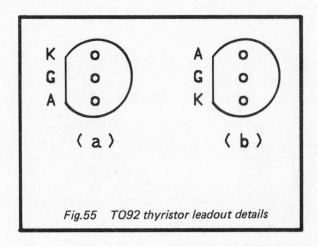

Fig.55   TO92 thyristor leadout details

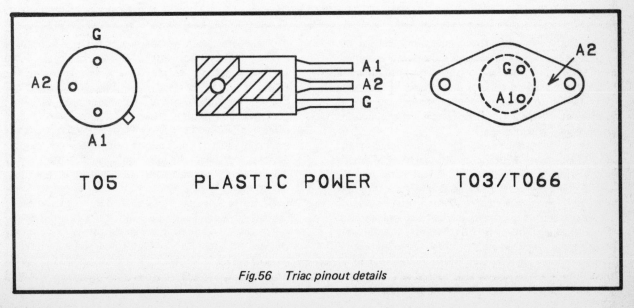

Fig.56   Triac pinout details

The printed circuit board has played a major part in the advance of electronics over the last few decades. It made possible mass production of complex pieces of equipment at relatively low cost. The complexity of printed circuit boards has generally increased over the years, with the introduction first of double-sided boards, and then of multi-layer types. The density of tracks and pads has also increased, with both getting ever smaller, as do the gaps between them. Of course, the components themselves have also steadily reduced in size, making high density printed circuit boards usable in practice.

A relatively recent development, although one which dates back further than many seem to realise, is the surface mount printed circuit board. This type

effectively take tracks from one side of the board through to the other. These boards are not double-sided in the sense that they have components on both sides of the board. It is very rare for this type of board to have components on both sides, and this complicates construction while giving very little advantage. Except in a very limited fashion, it is not possible to have an area of board occupied by components on both the top and bottom sides. Fitting components on both sides would therefore permit little increase in the package density, and in some cases would permit no increase in package density at all.

Surface mount integrated circuits are normally of the "flat-pack" type, and are soldered to the top side

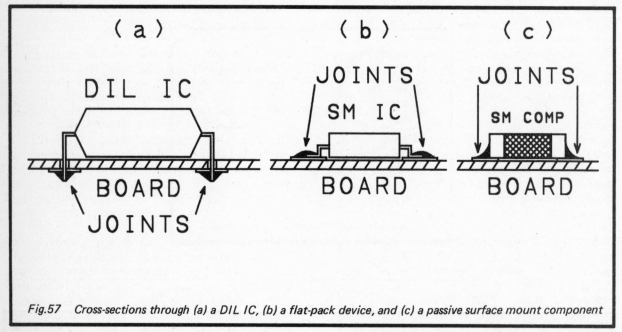

Fig.57   Cross-sections through (a) a DIL IC, (b) a flat-pack device, and (c) a passive surface mount component

of board is something that came about due to the search for ways of producing increasingly compact printed circuit boards. Apart from producing a smaller finished product, the shorter connecting tracks/leads of surface mount boards can be of significant advantage in high frequency applications (both digital and analogue).

The term "surface mounting" is to a large extent self-explanatory. With a conventional printed circuit board there are holes for the leadout wires or pins of the components, and the general scheme of things is to have the components mounted on one side of the board with the copper tracks/pads and connections on the other. In other words, the familiar arrangement depicted in the cross-section of Figure 57(a). With a double-sided board there are copper tracks on both sides of the board, with through-plated holes (or holes fitted with through-pins) to

of the board, as shown in Figure 57(b). Note that unlike conventional integrated circuits and their DIL packages, things are, as yet, less standardised in the world of surface mount integrated circuits. Consequently there are a large number of different packages in common use. Flat-pack devices are often called FPPs (Flat Plastic Packages), and originally had 1 millimetre pin spacing. Some devices now have the pins on a smaller pitch, and devices with around one hundred pins are not unknown!

There is a similar type of device called the SOP (Small Outline Package), and this is sometimes called by the alternative name of SOIC (Small Outline Integrated Circuit). These are very similar to standard DIL integrated circuits, but they have half the pin and row spacing. The pins in a row are therefore on a 0.05 inch pitch, and the two rows are

0.15 or 0.3 inches apart, depending on the number of pins. Of course, SOPs have flat-pack style pins, and not the DIL type that require holes in the board. As many TTL and CMOS devices are now produced in SOP versions, as are some analogue devices such as small audio amplifiers, these are the types which are most likely to appear in designs for the home constructor.

Passive surface mount components are also produced, including resistors, capacitors, and inductors. These are generally in the form of simple box shaped components having metal electrodes at each end, and they are connected to the board in the manner shown in Figure 57(c). There are also integrated circuits which have this type of leadless package, and these are known as LCCCs (Leadless Ceramic Chip Carriers).

Transistors for surface mounting are also manufactured, and these are usually rather like "flat-pack" integrated circuits, but with only three or four pins (if pins is the right term?). Devices of this type have been available to the home constructor for some time, and these seem to invariably be transistors for very high frequency operation. Leadless or practically leadless construction is virtually essential at these high frequencies, where it avoids problems due to inductance in the connecting leads.

Density

In terms of package density, surface mounting offers significant advantages. These are primarily due to the ability to have components on both sides of the board with few restrictions on their placement. For example, with a conventional board it is not possible to have a row of integrated circuits on one side of the board with another row at the same position on the underside of the board. Both sets of chips would require mounting holes at the same positions on the board, which is clearly impossible. Offsetting one set of chips slightly might seem to be the answer, but there could still be problems with connections to one set of devices seriously interfering with connections to the other set. More importantly, with one set of chips in place there would be no way of getting at the board to solder in the second set!

With surface mounting there is no problems, since each component only occupies one side of the board. It does obstruct things slightly in that the area occupied by a component is to some extent unusable for through-board connections, but things are far less restricted with this method of construction. I suppose that in an extreme case it would be possible to design two single-sided surface mount board layouts, and then to have these on opposite sides of a single board!

Home Construction

Surface mount boards and components were developed very much with commercial production in mind, and in particular with a view to application in high volume automatic production systems. For both home and commercial production of boards there is

the obvious advantage that no holes have to be drilled for the component leads and pins. As far as automated production techniques are concerned, a far greater advantage is the lack of any need to thread leadout wires or pins through holes in the board. This type of thing is quite difficult to achieve reliably automatically, and some components (such as 40 pin DIL integrated circuits) can often be quite awkward to fit by hand. The pads are generally smaller with surface mount boards, but accurate placement is still achieved much more easily than with a conventional board with its holes and leadout wires. Minor misalignment of components is quite tolerable with surface mount boards, and will not give problems such as the buckled integrated circuit pins that would occur with conventional boards. Surface mount boards are generally accepted as being more hardy than a conventional equivalent, especially where problems with vibration are likely to be encountered. This is due to the smaller and lighter construction of surface mount components.

In commercial production surface mount boards are not usually assembled by hand, and special equipment is used to position and fix the components in place ready for soldering. With an ordinary printed circuit board the components are normally held in place sufficiently well by virtue of their leadout wires being inserted through holes in the board to permit automatic soldering. This is not the case with surface mount components, and the normal way of fixing them in place ready for soldering is to use adhesive. The adhesive must be applied to parts of the components that are well away from the electrodes so that contamination of the soldered joints is avoided.

For both orthodox and surface mount boards, the usual method of automatic soldering is a "wave" type of some kind. This consists basically of suspending the board over a bath of molten solder, and then producing a wave which runs along the board, soldering the components in place as it goes. In practice more than one wave is often used in order to ensure reliable connections, and some preprocessing of the board is used to make sure this flux-free method of soldering works well. With some systems the solder bath has agitators which produce what might be termed "permanent waves", and the boards are drawn over the waves. With surface mount boards there is an obvious difference to conventional types with these methods of soldering, and this is that the solder is applied to the component side (or sides) of the board. Surface mount components for this type of construction have to be manufactured to withstand much higher temperatures than most conventional components can tolerate.

There are other methods of automatic soldering that can be utilized with surface mount boards, and with one of these the adhesive used to fix the components in place is applied to the electrodes, and it contains a large amount of powdered solder.

This form of adhesive is known as "solder paste", and the idea is that by heating the board to about 250 degrees or so the solder is made to flow and effectively convert the adhesive joints into proper soldered types. Systems of this type are called "reflow" assembly methods. They differ in the methods used to heat the board (or in some cases just the joints are heated). Probably the most common method is the "vapour phase" one, where the board is placed in a chamber of inert boiling liquid, but in the vapour above the liquid rather than in the liquid itself. Other methods use hot jets of air, infra-red heaters, special soldering tools, and lasers.

Surface mount technology has undoubted advantages for large scale commercial production, but is it a viable proposition for the electronics enthusiast? Clearly many commercial methods of production require a lot of specialised and expensive equipment that makes them totally impractical as far as the home constructor is concerned. The high temperatures involved in some of these methods necessitates the use of boards made from special materials, and a lot of other specialised components and materials are required.

Despite these problems, it is possible for the home constructor to produce surface mount printed circuit boards. The boards themselves can be produced using conventional techniques, and although commercial boards tend to use very fine and densely packed tracks, this is not mandatory. The range of surface mount components available to the home constructor is very limited at present, and this is probably the main limiting factor for anyone wishing to produce their own surface mount projects. However, some components are available, and an increasing range of components should become available as surface mount construction gains in popularity with both commercial and private users.

Assuming a board can be produced, and the components to fit onto it can be obtained, this leaves only the obstacle of actually fitting the components onto the board. Most surface components can be soldered in place using a conventional soldering iron and solder, but fine gauge solder and an iron fitted with a very narrow bit (about 1 millimetre) are required. Soldering components in place on a conventional board can be rather awkward, being something of a three-handed job. Soldering surface mount components in place is certainly no less awkward. Again it is something of a three-handed job, with one being needed to hold the component in place, the second being required to wield the soldering iron, and the third feeding in the solder. The very small size of the components compounds the problems. With patience and a lot of care it is possible to solder the components in place. Some means of clipping them in place is needed, or with some components (the larger ones such as many of the semiconductors) they can be glued in place using Super-Glue or a similar adhesive. The problem with gluing them in place is that it might prove to be impossible to remove them if a mistake is made or the board needs servicing.

Surface mount technology is certainly gaining ground, but it has not advanced anything like as rapidly as predicted by many two or three years ago. Nevertheless, it is likely to gradually take over in the commercial production of boards, and some recently released semiconductors have only been made available in surface mount versions. There seems little likelihood of conventional components disappearing from the market in the short or medium term, and those who wish to continue using orthodox constructional techniques should be able to do so for many years to come.

For the home constructor the use of surface mount devices is something of an adventure at present, and this method of construction is not practical for regular use. This situation seems almost certain to change though, and a wider range of components should gradually come onto the market. Of equal importance, tools and equipment to make surface mount construction easier and a more practical method for hand assembly of boards should be developed and marketed. While the small size of components enables very compact boards to be produced, it makes things very difficult as far as hand assembly is concerned. For DIL integrated circuits the pins in each row are 0.1 inch apart, but with surface mount devices 0.05 inch pitch is the nearest thing to a standard pitch. Some devices have electrodes spaced by only about half this amount. A surface mount resistor is typically only about 3.2 millimetres by 1.6 millimetres. For hand assembly this small size possibly represents the greatest difficulty, and optical aids to construction might become as essential as some form of soldering tool.

At present we can only guess about the way in which the problems of small scale production using surface mount technology will be tackled. In the mean time this method of construction certainly represents an interesting challenge for the more adventurous enthusiasts.

In this section a number of useful electronic building blocks are described, including such things as oscillators and filters. There is only enough space available to cover a selection of the most common types of circuit block, but readers who require a larger range of circuits are referred to the books 'Practical Electronic Building Blocks — Book 1', and 'Practical Electronic Building Blocks — Book 2' (BP117 and BP118 respectively), from the same publisher and author as this book.

555

The 555 timer integrated circuit seems to be present in a substantial proportion of designs published for the home constructor, as well as many items of ready-made equipment. This is not really surprising when one considers its versatility and low cost. Its most simple mode of operation is the monostable type, as shown in the circuit diagram of Figure 58.

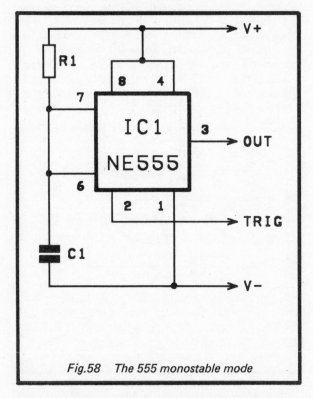

Fig.58   The 555 monostable mode

This is triggered by taking the trigger input below one-third of the supply voltage, and the positive output pulse from pin 3 is then governed by the values of timing components R1 and C1. The circuit is of the retriggerable variety, which means that if the input is still below the trigger threshold at the end of the timing pulse, a new timing run is immediately commenced. In other words the circuit can only be used as a pulse lengthener and can not operate as a pulse shortener.

The timing period in seconds is equal to 1.1 CR, where C is the value of C1 in farads, and R is the value of R1 in ohms. In practice it is easier to deal with the values of these components in microfarads and megohms respectively. As a simple example, values of 1μ and 1M would obviously give a pulse duration of 1.1 seconds. Other times can be obtained by making proportionate changes to the values of R1 and (or) C1. For instance, a pulse length of 2 milliseconds (0.002 seconds) would require the time constant to be reduced by a factor of 550. This could be achieved by reducing R1 by a factor of (say) 11 to give a value of 100k, and reducing C1 by a factor of fifty to give a value of 50n. Obviously the required values will not always be preferred ones (as in this case), and then the nearest preferred value must be used. Thus C1 would have to be 47n and not 50n, or the value would need to be made up from several components such as two 100n capacitors in series. Where good accuracy is needed it will usually be necessary to have R1 adjustable so that it can be trimmed to give precisely the required pulse duration.

C1 can be an electrolytic component (with the negative terminal connected to the negative supply), but high values for C1 and R1 to give long pulse durations are often impractical due to the leakage in the capacitor. Times of up to a few minutes can be achieved though. R1 must not be less than a few hundred ohms in value so as to limit the current flow through R1 and into IC1 in the quiescent state to a safe figure. In many cases the value of R1 must be much higher than this in order to keep the current consumption of the unit down to an acceptable figure.

The supply voltage range for the standard 555 is 4 to 16 volts, and the output can source or sink 200 milliamps. The minimum practical pulse duration is about 1 microsecond and the typical rise and fall time of the output pulse are both 100ns. Note that 'improved' versions of the 555 are available, such as the ICM7555. This is a low power CMOS type which has only about one-hundredth of the standard components' current consumption (about 80μA as opposed to 8mA) and it does not produce the switching glitches on the supply rails that are associated with the standard device. The maximum output source current is only a few milliamps though.

The other main mode of the 555 is the astable (oscillator) mode, as shown in the circuit diagram of Figure 59. Here C1 charges to two-thirds of the supply voltage via R1 and R2, and then it discharges to one-third of the supply voltage via R2 and an internal switching transistor of IC1. C1 then charges via R1 and R2 again, and the circuit oscillates in this way indefinitely. The output goes high during the charge period and low during the discharge period. Note that as C1 is charged by way of both timing

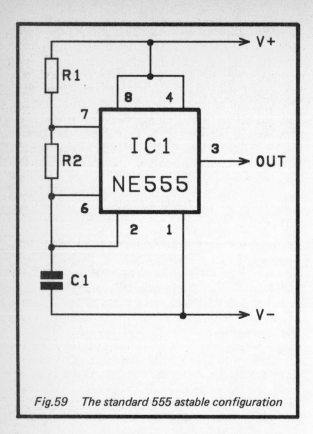

Fig.59   The standard 555 astable configuration

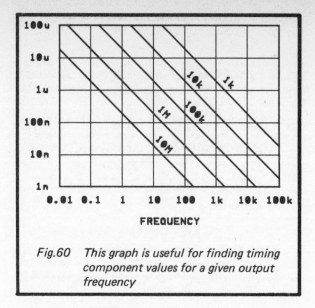

Fig.60   This graph is useful for finding timing component values for a given output frequency

resistors, but is discharged only through R2, the output of this basic configuration can never be a proper squarewave with an accurate 1:1 mark-space ratio. Making R1 low in value when compared to R2 will give something close to a squarewave output, but R1 can not be made very low in value as this would give an excessive current flow through this component and into IC1 during the discharge period.

The frequency of oscillation is given by the formula:—

$$f = 1.44/(R1 + 2R2) C$$

In practice it is often easier to use a chart such as the one shown in Figure 60 when selecting the timing component values. The resistances shown here are the total timing resistances (i.e. R1 added to twice R2), and lines for other resistances could easily be marked onto this chart if necessary. In the astable mode the 555 will operate up to a frequency of at least 500kHz.

If a gated oscillator is required, the gate signal can be applied to pin 4 of IC1. A high signal enables oscillation, a low signal disables the oscillator. The circuit can be frequency modulated by applying the modulation signal to pin 5 of IC1.

CMOS

CMOS logic integrated circuits are a versatile range of components which includes such things as monostable and astable devices. However, it is often possible to use

a couple of spare gates or inverters to operate as astable or monostable circuits with an adequate level of performance. Figure 61 shows the standard astable configuration, and this is shown as being based on two 2 input NOR gates. These are simply wired as inverters though, and NAND gates similarly connected or 'real' CMOS inverters will operate just as well. The operating frequency is roughly equal to 1/1.4 C R Hertz, but only roughly.

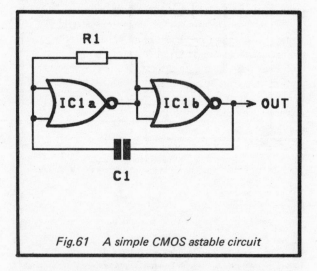

Fig.61   A simple CMOS astable circuit

The standard CMOS monostable configuration is shown in Figure 62. This is a positive edge triggered type, and is not a retriggerable type like the 555. In other words, it is triggered as the input is taken from the low state to the high state. Leaving the input high will not cause a new output pulse to be commenced when the first one has finished, and the circuit can therefore operate as both a pulse lengthener and a pulse shortener. The output pulse duration is approximately 0.68 C R seconds. The output pulse is a positive type, but adding an inverter

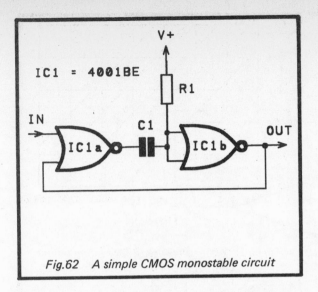

Fig.62   A simple CMOS monostable circuit

here gives the usual Q and not Q outputs. Adding an inverter at the input makes the circuit negative edge triggered. Note that IC1a is used as a 2 input NOR gate and not as an inverter; and that this circuit is therefore only usable with a NOR gate device such as the 4001BE.

Audio Amplifiers

For audio pre-amplification operational amplifiers offer what is often the best choice, but as these are dealt with in a separate section of this book they will not be considered here. Discrete transistor designs are frequently a viable alternative to operational amplifiers, but they are less easy to deal with from the design point of view, and the ease with which the gain and input impedance of operational amplifiers can be set makes them a more realistic choice for most users. However, the common emitter amplifier of Figure 63 is a useful electronic

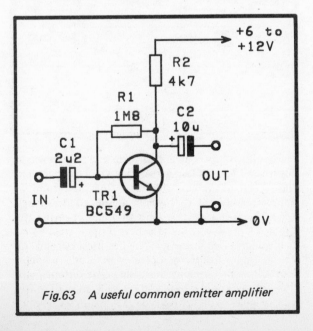

Fig.63   A useful common emitter amplifier

building block which offers typically a little over 40dB of voltage gain, an input impedance of around 12 kilohms, and an output impedance of 4.7 kilohms. The BC549 is a low noise device and the circuit is suitable for use with low level audio signals. The gain can be reduced by adding a resistor between the emitter of TR1 and the negative supply rail. The voltage gain is equal to the value of the collector load resistor divided by the emitter resistance, but there is an internal emitter resistance of around 40 ohms which must be added to any external resistance. A byproduct of the negative feedback introduced by an emitter resistor is an increase in the input impedance and reduced distortion.

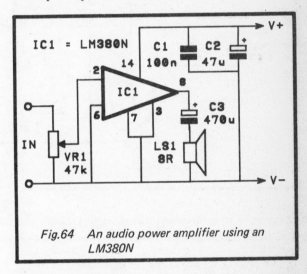

Fig.64   An audio power amplifier using an LM380N

Probably the most popular audio power amplifier integrated circuit is the LM380N, and this operates in the basic circuit shown in Figure 64. No D.C. blocking capacitor is needed between the input of the device and volume control VR1, but D.C. signals must be blocked from VR1 by adding a 470n capacitor into the signal path if necessary. The voltage gain is fixed at 34dB (50 times). The supply voltage range is 8 to 22 volts, and with an 18 volt supply it will deliver 2 watts R.M.S. into an 8 ohm load with 0.2% distortion. The device incorporates both output short circuit and thermal overload protection circuits. When used with noisy power supplies a 10μ capacitor should be connected between pin 1 and earth to improve the supply ripple rejection.

For applications where a small power amplifier capable of operating on low supply voltages is needed the TBA820M is a popular choice. This operates in the circuit which appears in Figure 65. Note that IC1 must be a TBA820M and not a TBA820.

This circuit will operate over a 3 to 12 volt supply range, and it will provide 2 watts R.M.S. into an 8 ohm load with a 12 volt supply. It is more useful at lower supply voltages though, where most other audio power amplifier chips fail to work at all. An attractive feature is a typical quiescent current consumption of only 4 milliamps, and this makes the

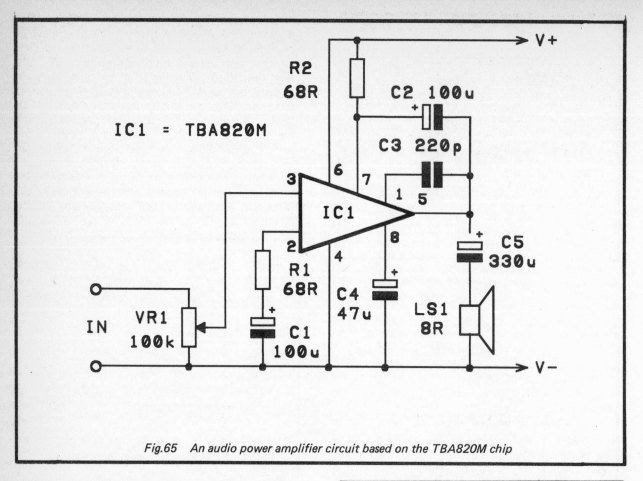

Fig.65   *An audio power amplifier circuit based on the TBA820M chip*

circuit well suited to applications where battery operation is needed. The voltage gain of the circuit is about 40dB, but within reason this can be adjusted by varying the value of R1 (variations in its value having an inversely proportional effect on the voltage gain). The TBA820M does not have output short circuit or thermal protection circuits incidentally.

Filters

Figure 66 shows the basic single stage lowpass (a) and highpass (b) filter circuits. The specified values give a cutoff frequency of about 1kHz in both cases, but other frequencies can be obtained by altering the value of the resistor and (or) the capacitor. Changing the value of either the resistor or the capacitor gives an inversely proportional change in the cutoff frequency.

These basic filters are little used these days as they give only a very gradual initial roll-off, and will only work properly if they are fed from a low impedance and feed into a high impedance. Active filters give much better performance with a much sharper introduction of the full attenuation rate, and a low output impedance. They still require a reasonably low source impedance though, and must be preceded by a buffer stage where necessary. Two stage active lowpass and highpass filter circuits are shown in Figures 67 and 68 respectively. Three

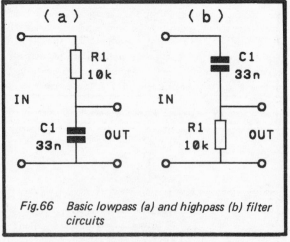

Fig.66   *Basic lowpass (a) and highpass (b) filter circuits*

stage (18dB per octave) equivalents are shown in Figures 69 and 70 respectively. With all these designs the specified values give a cutoff frequency at approximately 1kHz. Like the simple passive filters, other frequencies can be obtained by changing the values of the resistors and (or) capacitors. However, it is a matter of changing all the resistor values or all the capacitor values in proportion to one another, and not just altering the value of a single component.

With the lowpass filters no input biasing is shown, and in many cases direct connection to the previous

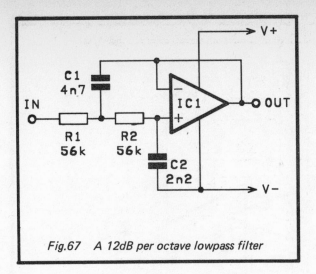

Fig.67 A 12dB per octave lowpass filter

stage is acceptable, with this stage providing a suitable quiescent bias voltage. Where appropriate though, a potential divider to bias the input must be included, together with an input coupling capacitor. Virtually any operational amplifier can be used in these circuits, but as the device is used at unity gain it makes sense to use a fully internally compensated type. The standard 741C is adequate for most purposes, but a higher quality type such as the LF351 can be used if very low noise and distortion levels are needed. Note that C — R filters are normally only used at frequencies of up to about 100kHz or so. At higher frequencies stray capacitance and inductance can result in highly unpredictable results.

Pinout details for the LM380N, TBA820M and NE555 devices are provided in Figure 71.

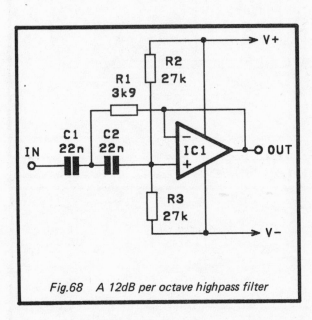

Fig.68 A 12dB per octave highpass filter

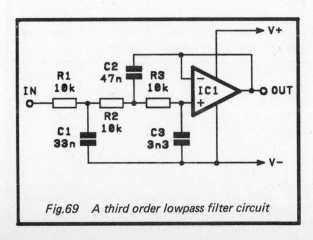

Fig.69 A third order lowpass filter circuit

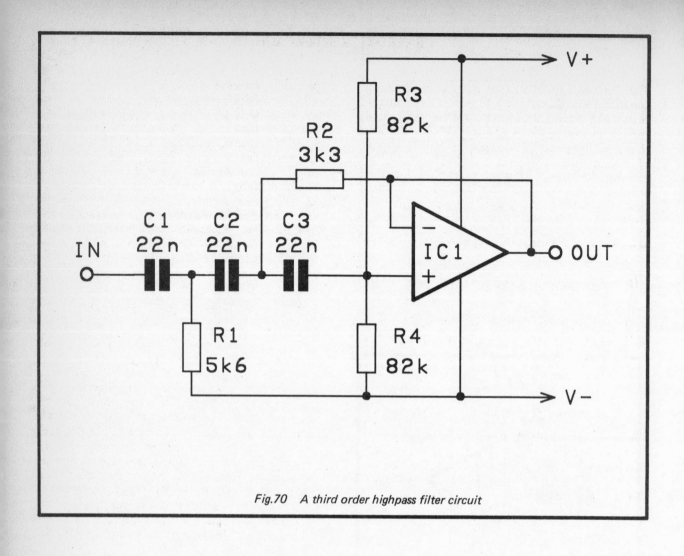

Fig.70   *A third order highpass filter circuit*

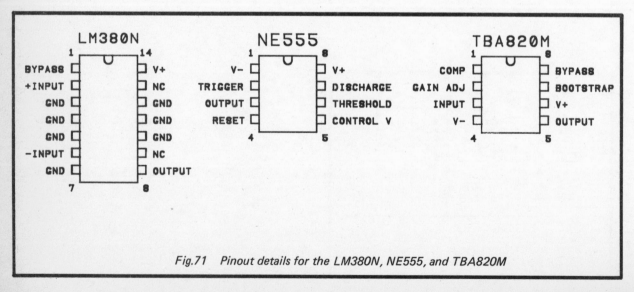

Fig.71   *Pinout details for the LM380N, NE555, and TBA820M*

CENTRONICS INTERFACE

The Centronics (parallel) type interface is the most common form of computer to printer communications link. It uses a 36-way connector which uses the pin numbering shown in Figure 72 (this diagram shows the terminals as seen looking onto the front of a Centronics type plug, or onto the rear of a Centronics socket). Not all computers use the standard 36-way connector for their parallel printer port, but I have yet to come across a printer or plotter which deviates from this standard.

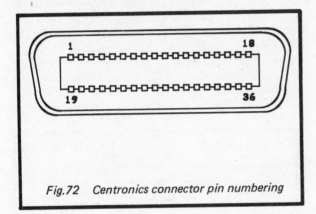

Fig.72   Centronics connector pin numbering

The pin connections are as follows:—

Pin	Function
1	Strobe
2	Data 0
3	Data 1
4	Data 2

Pin	Function
5	Data 3
6	Data 4
7	Data 5
8	Data 6
9	Data 7
10	Acknowledge
11	Busy
12	Paper Empty
13	Selected Output
14	No Connection
15	No Connection
16	Ground
17	Ground
18	+5V
19 to 29	Ground (to act as screens)
30	Ground
31	No Connection
32	Fault Output
33 to 36	No Connection

For a basic communications link only the eight data lines, the strobe line, a single ground connection, and either the 'Busy' or 'Acknowledge' handshake lines are required. If a ribbon cable is used to make the connections the numerous ground terminals connect to leads which act as screens between the signal leads. Note that the minor functions such as 'Paper Empty' are not implemented on all equipment, and that the precise function can vary from one piece of equipment to another. Parallel links of this type are only recommended for use over a range of 2 metres or less.

RS232C INTERFACE

The standard RS232C serial interface uses a 25-way D connector, but the pin numbering is different for the male and female connectors, as detailed in Figure 73. Both show the numbering for the rear view of a connector (i.e. as seen when looking onto the pins and wiring up a connector). Note that many pieces of equipment which have RS232C or compatible serial ports do not use this type of connector at all.

Pin	Function
9 to 13	No Connection
14	Secondary Transmitted Data
15	No Connection
16	Secondary Received Data
17 to 19	No Connection
20	Data Terminal Ready
21 to 25	No Connection

Unlike the Centronics system, this is a two-way interface. In its most basic form it is just a matter of connecting the two signal ground terminals and cross coupling the transmitted data and received data terminals. In most cases one or more of the handshake lines must be implemented in order to give a controlled data flow. Typical RS232C interconnections are shown in Figure 74, but some equipment requires a slightly different arrangement, and it is

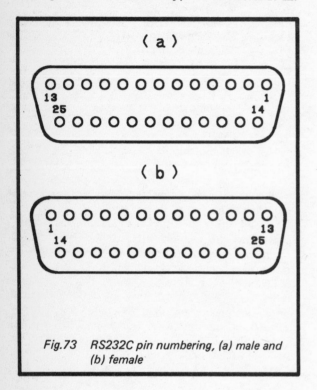

Fig.73   RS232C pin numbering, (a) male and (b) female

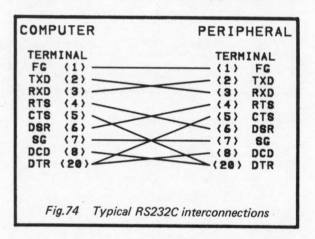

Fig.74   Typical RS232C interconnections

Pin functions for the standard 25-way connector are as follows:—

Pin	Function
1	Protective Ground
2	Transmitted Data
3	Received Data
4	Request To Send
5	Clear To Send
6	Data Set Ready
7	Signal Ground
8	Received Line Signal Detector

advisable to follow any manufacturer's recommendations for the equipment you are using. In particular, some equipment receives data on the 'Transmitted Data' pin and transmits it on the 'Received Data' pin. The idea of this is that a cable without any crossed over connections can be used to connect together two pieces of equipment having complementary ports.

The RS232C system will operate over a distance of at least 15 metres at high transmission rates, and will operate over much longer distances at low baud rates.

AMATEUR BAND ALLOCATIONS

Short Wave

Band	Frequency Range
160 Metres	1.8 to 2.0 MHz
80 Metres	3.5 to 3.8 MHz (4 MHz)
40 Metres	7 to 7.1 MHz (7.3 MHz)
30 Metres	10.1 to 10.15 MHz
20 Metres	14 to 14.35 MHz
17 Metres	18.068 to 18.168 MHz
15 Metres	21 to 21.45 MHz
12 Metres	24.89 to 24.99 MHz
10 Metres	28 to 29.7 MHz

These are the Region 1 allocations (which are appropriate to the U.K.). In some other areas, particularly the U.S.A., larger bands are in operation. The figures in brackets indicate the extents of the larger bands.

V.H.F.

Band	Frequency Range
6 Metres	50 to 52 MHz
4 Metres	70.025 to 70.5 MHz
2 Metres	144 to 146 MHz

CB FREQUENCY ALLOCATIONS

27 MHz Band

Channel	Frequency (MHz)
1	27.60125
2	27.61125
3	27.62125
4	27.63125
5	27.64125
6	27.65125
7	27.66125
8	27.67125
9	27.68125
10	27.69125
11	27.70125
12	27.71125
13	27.72125
14	27.73125
15	27.74125
16	27.75125
17	27.76125
18	27.77125
19	27.78125
20	27.79125
21	27.80125
22	27.81125
23	27.82125
24	27.83125
25	27.84125
26	27.85125
27	27.86125
28	27.87125
29	27.88125
30	27.89125
31	27.90125
32	27.91125

Channel	Frequency (Mhz)
33	27.92125
34	27.93125
35	27.94125
36	27.95125
37	27.96125
38	27.97125
39	27.98125
40	27.99125

934 MHz Band

Channel	Frequency (Mhz)
1	934.025
2	934.075
3	934.125
4	934.175
5	934.225
6	934.275
7	934.325
8	934.375
9	934.425
10	934.475
11	934.525
12	934.575
13	934.625
14	934.675
15	934.725
16	934.775
17	934.825
18	934.875
19	934.925
20	934.975

AMATEUR ABBREVIATIONS

Amateur abbreviations were originally used to enable messages in Morse Code to be sent in a more compact form. They are still used for Morse Code communications, but many (XYL for example) are now used much more generally by the radio amateur fraternity. This list gives details of many of the more common amateur abbreviations.

ABT	About
AGN	Again
ALC	Automatic level control
AM	Amplitude modulation
ANI	Any
ANT	Antenna
ARS	Amateur radio society
BC	Broadcast
BCI	Broadcast interference
BCNU	Bee seeing you
BFO	Beat frequency oscillator
BK	Break
BT	Battery
BW	Bandwidth
B4	Before
CANS	Headphones
CCT	Circuit
CK	Check
CLG	Calling
CO	Crystal oscilator
CQ	Request for someone to respond to a transmission
CONDX	Conditions
CUAGN	See you again
CUL	See you later
CUD	Could
CW	Continuous wave (Morse code)
DE	From
DET	Detector (demodulator)
DF	Direction finder
DSB	Double sideband
DX	Long distance or otherwise difficult communications
ERE	Here
ES	And
FB	Fine business
FD	Field day
FM	Frequency modulation
FR	For
FONE	Telephony (i.e. voice communications)
GA	Go ahead or good afternoon
GB	Goodbye
GE	Good evening
GG	Going
GLD	Glad
GM	Good morning
GND	Ground (earth)

GUD	Good
HI	Laughter, high spirits
HPE	Hope
HR	Hear hear
HRD	Heard
HV	Have
HW	How
ID	Identification
IF	Intermediate frequency
KHZ	Kilohertz
LID	Bad operator
MNI	Many
MS	Meteor Scatter
MSG	Message
MHZ	Megahertz
ND	Nothing doing
NW	Now
OB	Old boy
OG	Old girl
OM	Old man
OP	Operator
OT	Old timer
PA	Power amplifier
PSE	Please
R	Everything received correctly
RPT	Report
RX	Receiver
SA	Say
SED	Said
SIGS	Signals
SRI	Sorry
SSB	Single sideband
SUM	Some
SWL	Short wave listener
TKS	Thanks
TMW	Tomorrow
TNX	Thanks
TT	That
TU	Thank you
TVI	Television interference
TX	Transmitter
U	You
UR	You are
VFO	Variable frequency oscillator
VXO	Variable crystal oscillator
VY	Very
WID	With
WKD	Worked
WL	Will
WUD	Would
WX	Weather
XYL	Wife (ex-young lady)
YF	Wife
YL	Young Lady
73	Best wishes
88	Love and kisses

Q CODES

The Q codes are not exclusively used by radio amateurs, and are generally used in the field of radio communications. They were originally devised to streamline Morse Code communications, but are used more generally these days. They are used to answer questions, as in the list below, but can also be used as an answer or an instruction. Some have become general terms. For example, QRP can mean "shall I reduce power", but it can also be the response "decrease power", and it is also used by radio amateurs as a general term for low power operation.

QRA   What is the name of your station?

QRB   What is your approximate distance from my station?

QRH   Does my frequency fluctuate?

QRI   Is my note good?

QRK   Are you receiving me well? (Also used by amateurs as an abbreviation for money!)

QRL   Are you busy?

QRM   Is my signal contaminated with man-made interference (adjacent channel interference etc.)?

QRN   Is my signal subject to atmospheric interference?

QRO   Do you wish me to increase power? (Also used as an abbreviation for high powered transmitter operation.)

QRP   Do you wish me to reduce power? (Also used as an abbreviation for low powered transmitter operation.)

QRQ   Shall I send faster?

QRS   Shall I send slower?

QRT   Shall I stop sending? (Also used to signify that a station is closing down.)

QRV   Are you ready?

QRX   Shall I wait?

QRZ   Who is calling me?

QSB   Does my signal vary in strength? (Also used as an abbreviation for signal fading.)

QSL   Did you copy that? (Also the name of a card sent as confirmation of a contact, or to acknowledge a reception report.)

QSO   A contact with another station.

QSP   Will you relay this message to . . . ?

QSV   Shall I send a series of Vs?

QSZ   Shall I send each group of words twice?

QSY   Shall I change frequency?

QTH   What is your location? (Also used as a general abbreviation for the address from which radio amateur operates his or her station.)

QTR   What is the time?

SINPO

SINPO is a form of brief reception report, and it rates five aspects of the signal on a 1 to 5 scale. These five aspects are signal strength (S), interference (I), noise (N), propagation disturbance (P), and over-all readability (O). Rating details for all five of these are given below.

Signal Strength
1   Only just audible
2   Poor
3   Fair
4   Good
5   Excellent

Interference
1   Extremely bad
2   Severe
3   Moderate
4   Slight
5   None

Noise
1   Extremely bad
2   Severe
3   Moderate
4   Slight
5   None

Propagation Disturbance
1   Extremely bad
2   Severe
3   Moderate
4   Slight
5   None

Overall Rating
1   Unreadable
2   Poor
3   Fair
4   Good
5   Excellent

MORSE CODE

A	.−	4	....−
B	−...	5	.....
C	−.−.	6	−....
D	−..	7	−−...
E	.	8	−−−..
F	..−.	9	−−−−.
G	−−.	0	−−−−−
H	....		
I	..	Apostrophe	.−−−−.
J	.−−−	Bracket	−.−−.−
K	−.−	Break sign	−...−
L	.−..	Comma	−−..−−
M	−−	End of message	.−.−.
N	−.	End of work	...−.−
O	−−−	Error	....
P	.−−.	Full stop	.−.−.−.
Q	−−.−	Hyphen	−....−
R	.−.	Inverted commas	.−..−.
S	...	Question mark	..−−..
T	−	Understood	...−.
U	..−	Wait	.−...
V	...−		
W	.−−		
X	−..−	A dot equals one unit of time.
Y	−.−−	A dash equals three units of time.
Z	−−..	The space between dots/dashes forming a character is one unit of time.
1	.−−−−	
2	..−−−	The space between characters equals three units of time.
3	...−−	The space between two words equal five units of time.

FREQUENCY — WAVELENGTH CONVERSION

MHz	Metres		MHz	Metres
1	300		19	15.79
1.1	272.7		20	15
1.2	250		21	14.29
1.3	230.8		22	13.64
1.4	214.3		23	13.04
1.5	200		24	12.5
1.6	187.5		25	12
1.7	176.5		26	11.54
1.8	166.6		27	11.11
1.9	157.9		28	10.71
2	150		29	10.34
2.5	120		30	10
3	100			
3.5	86			
4	75			
4.5	66.6			
5	60			
5.5	54.5			
6	50			
6.5	46.2			
7	42.9			
7.5	40			
8	37.5			
8.5	35.3			
9	33.3			
9.5	31.6			
10	30			
11	27.27			
12	25			
13	23.08			
14	21.43			
15	20			
16	18.75			
17	17.65			
18	16.88			

Frequencies outside the range of this table can be accommodated without too much difficulty. For example, a frequency of 100MHz is tens times higher than 10MHz, and the wavelength will therefore be only one-tenth as long at 100MHz. The wavelength at 10MHz is 30 metres, and at 100MHz it will consequently be 3 metres (30 metres divided 10 equals 3 metres). Frequency to wavelength conversion is quite straightforward anyway, and to convert from megahertz to metres simply divide 300 by the frequency (e.g. 300 divided by 4MHz equals 75 metres). To convert kilohertz to metres divide 300000 by the frequency (e.g. 300000 divided by 100kHz equals 3000 metres).

Wavelength to frequency conversion is equally simple. Dividing 300 by the wavelength in metres gives an answer in megahertz, or dividing 300000 by the wavelength in metres gives an answer in kilohertz. For instance, 150 metres is equivalent to 2MHz (300 divided by 150 metres equals 2MHz) or 2000kHz (300000 divided by 150 metres equals 2000kHz).

FREE CATALOGUE

If you would like, free of charge, a complete catalogue of our entire range of Radio, Electronics and Computer books, then please send a stamped addressed envelope to:—

BERNARD BABANI (publishing) LTD
THE GRAMPIANS
SHEPHERDS BUSH ROAD
LONDON W6 7NF
ENGLAND